SPACE AGE DICTIONARY

Edited by

CHARLES McLAUGHLIN

President, McLaughlin Research Corporation
New York, N. Y.

D. VAN NOSTRAND COMPANY, INC.

PRINCETON, NEW JERSEY

TORONTO   LONDON

NEW YORK

D. VAN NOSTRAND COMPANY, INC.
120 Alexander St., Princeton, New Jersey (*Principal office*)
257 Fourth Avenue, New York 10, New York

D. VAN NOSTRAND COMPANY, LTD.
358, Kensington High Street, London, W.14, England

D. VAN NOSTRAND COMPANY (Canada), LTD.
25 Hollinger Road, Toronto 16, Canada

Published simultaneously in Canada by
D. VAN NOSTRAND COMPANY (Canada), LTD.

Library of Congress Catalogue Card No. 59-14613

PRINTED IN THE UNITED STATES OF AMERICA

PREFACE

This book has been prepared to meet the need for an authoritative, up-to-date and yet concise dictionary of the salient terms in space technology. This new field comprises not only the missiles, satellites and other space vehicles, but also the major scientific principles and technological methods that have contributed to the advancing space frontier. It has therefore given rise to a new language, which is presented in these pages in a form for convenient reference.

All definitions have been expressed as clearly and simply as possible. To this end a considerable number of vivid illustrations have been prepared for this book. They are functional diagrams designed to contribute to an understanding of the principles explained in the text. There are also silhouettes of the U.S. missiles, which have been grouped in alphabetical order at the end of the book, following the alphabetically arranged dictionary of terms.

The Editor wishes to acknowledge the contributions of the many scientists and engineers who have helped to make this book possible. While space does not permit mention of all their names, he wishes to credit specifically the suggestions and work of Mr. O. C. Romanelli, Mr. S. M. Arwine, Mr. P. M. Barr, Mr. A. S. Newdorf, Mr. T. Haycock, Mr. E. E. Rose, Mr. R. Fanezzi, Mr. G. S. Gilbert, Mr. L. M. Perlman, Mr. F. J. Heinz, Miss Virginia Johnson.

New York, N. Y.   CHARLES MCLAUGHLIN
July, 1959

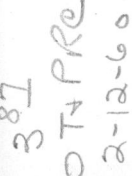

iii

490

FOREWORD

The development of missiles and aircraft has made enormous stride during the past twenty years. Propulsion systems based upon jet engines and rockets, especially the latter, have made possible the attainment of great speeds. In rocketry, the most spectacular development has been the ICBM which has carried its nose cone to distances of one quarter of the circumference of the earth, in periods of time on the order of one-half hour. Moreover, this monster missile has permitted the first step toward one of mankind's most persistent dreams: flight into outer space.

This first step is represented by the artificial satellites. A number of them have been launched successfully, by the USA and the USSR, some of which may well remain in orbit for years. Their contribution includes more than an advance toward space travel; for they have telemetered back to earth important information about upper atmospheric conditions that influence weather, as well as data on radiation, meteors and other phenomena far out in space.

Another major achievement has been the development of better and more diversified guidance systems. They include such well-known types as beam-rider, inertial, command, and homing systems, as well as many more specialized types such as star tracking, celestial navigation, Doppler, Doppler radar, and loran guidance systems. Some of these systems are standard navigation items used by aircraft pilots. When applied in missiles, they function entirely automatically for piloting, detonation and other purposes.

The high velocities which must be imparted to a missile for space flight can be judged from the fact that the "orbital velocity" which must be imparted to a body if it is to become a satellite of the earth at a distance of a few hundred miles from the surface, is about five miles per second. The velocity which a body must have to leave the earth and not return (the "escape velocity") is about seven miles per second. A body leaving the earth with this velocity would either become a satellite moving around the sun (that is to say, a small planet) or it might travel to the moon or some other celestial body, either to reach them or to go into orbit about them. In fact, several attempts have been made to launch a "lunar probe" (that is, a body which orbits about the moon). Such probes are equipped with instruments to telemeter to earth information about the moon's hidden side, as well as space data that should be helpful in later manned flights. The succcessful launching of such a "lunar probe" or of a "planetary probe" would constitute man's second step into space.

The third step into space will probably be putting first an animal, and then a man, into orbit and bringing them back alive. This operation poses the problem of re-entry into the earth's atmosphere. The two major hazards are that the animal or man might be incinerated by the heat, or that he might be crushed by the deceleration. Retrorockets are probably the solution. They would be operated by the passenger or, more probably, by remote control, and slow the satellite down gradually.

It must be added at this point that entering a planet's atmosphere, though difficult, is easier than landing on a planet without an atmosphere. Properly navigated, a spaceship can use the atmosphere as a cushion. A technique is being worked out by which a ship would spiral round the earth in ever-decreasing ellipses, alternately entering the atmosphere in order to brake its speed and leaving it in order to cool off, assisted by retrorockets for further braking. If the spaceship were landing on a planet without an atmosphere, the retrorockets would have to carry the whole burden of braking, and would require operation with pin-point accuracy.

In a satellite, a man will for the first time experience "weightlessness" over an extended period. How will weightlessness affect him? Will he become exhilarated or sick? We may know within a year. Other space survival problems will also be encountered for the first time: air and heat conditioning, protection against sunlight (without the screen of our atmosphere it would blind us), and against radiation, meteors, etc. The satellite will, of course, carry a two-way radio. At any time the passenger, if conscious, can say: "GET-ME-DOWN."

The fourth step into space may consist of the construction of a space station. This device would be a giant artificial satellite manned by a three or four man crew; it would probably rotate about a central axis to simulate gravity. It would carry instruments for making observations similar to those installed in present-day satellites, but on a more extensive scale. It would carry a telescope to observe distant celestial bodies, that can be seen from earth only dimly, if at all, because of the blanket of atmosphere. Such a space station would continually travel in an orbit about the earth; ferry rockets or ferry spaceships would travel to and fro between it and the earth, carrying personnel and supplies. Moreover, the space station would serve as a point of departure and return for high-efficiency, low-thrust spaceships especially designed for interplanetary flight.

The fifth step into space, which might well antedate the fourth, would be the journey of a manned spaceship around the moon. If this were done with present-day rocket fuels, the trip would be a severe ordeal for the man or men, for the ship could not be powered beyond the first few hundred miles, so that it would need to coast all the rest of the way to the moon and back (about 450,000 miles). That is, the passengers would be in "free fall" and thus experience weightlessness for almost the entire trip. The time required for speeds close to "escape velocity" would be a matter of days, and during all this time the passengers would experience the rigors of weightlessness and confinement as well as the physical hazards of radiation, meteors, excessive heat and cold and blinding sunlight, to mention but a few.

However, by use of the space station, flights around the moon, or to other distant points, can be made far more comfortable and safe for the passengers. They would only need a streamlined ship for the first and last few hundred miles of the trip—going from earth to the space station and, on the return journey, from the station to the earth. At the station they would change into a roomier, more commodious ship which would not be streamlined (since it would be used only in outer space) and travel in it between the station and the moon, or the planet visited. Moreover, takeoff would be much easier than from the earth, because the new ship need not accelerate to escape velocity from rest, but only from the orbital velocity of the space station.

The sixth step into space would be the landing of a man on a foreign celestial body. Most authorities think this will be the moon, although there are others who point out that a landing on Mars would be easier because of the latter's atmosphere. This is true—but there is the formidable question of time. A trip to Mars using present-day fuels would take over eight months.

Eventually, as fuels improve and higher velocities become attainable, we shall explore the whole solar system. Some day it is hoped that we shall be able to convert atomic energy directly into velocity of fuel exhaust without generating heat. This would do away with coasting; spaceships could then be powered throughout the whole voyage. A ship would accelerate at 32 feet per second throughout the first half of a trip, and decelerate at the same rate throughout the second half. This method of operation would reduce flight time enormously, and would also eliminate weightlessness, since the $1g$ acceleration would simulate gravity.

More fanciful speculations on space flight are concerning the use of the "photon sail" and "electrogravitics". The photon sail is a very thin, polished sheet of metal about one mile square, which would be "blown" along its course by the pressure of light from the sun. Unfortunately, calculations based upon present knowledge indicate that the acceleration so produced would be too small for practical needs. Electrogravitics is at present in the stage of pure speculation. It is the idea of a method whereby man will nullify existing gravitational fields and subject ships to "artificial" gravitational fields. If such a process were possible, it would certainly go far to advance space flight. Extremely high accelerations could be given to a ship without affecting the passengers. But new principles in science must first be discovered before such hopes can be realized.

Trips to fixed stars? That is quite different. The nearest star is four light years away; and the speed of light is 186,000 miles per second, immensely greater than the few miles per second attained by rockets now. But we might make some interstellar trips if the daring concept of "time dilatation" of the theory of relativity can be applied. By this principle, traveling at a speed very close to that of light might so slow down our clocks and metabolic processes that a year's journey would become a week's or a day's. The existence of time dilatation may be proved or disproved experimentally this year from data obtained on satellite-borne atomic clocks.

Space travel is on the way. Instruments have already been launched into space and are circling the earth, and the sun. Now it only remains for us to launch a man—the most complicated instrument of all. This should be achieved within the lifetime of people already born.

A

A-1, A-2, A-3, A-4, etc. A series of German missiles developed at Peenemunde during World War II. The most successful was the A-4, better known as the V-2. (*See also* V-1 and V-2.)

AAM. Air-to-air missile.

ablation. Latent heat of melting or vaporization. Certain missile NOSE CONES or portions thereof are coated with ablative material to make use of this vaporization in overcoming the thermal problems of RE-ENTRY.

ABMA. ARMY BALLISTIC MISSILE AGENCY.

abort. A failure during or after COUNT-DOWN which prevents a rocket from taking off and/or completing its mission.

acceleration due to gravity. The acceleration that a body, if not constrained, experiences due to its proximity to some other body.

The force between two particles (bodies that may be regarded as of point size) of mass m_1 and m_2, respectively (in grams), separated by a distance d (in centimeters), is given by

$$\text{force} = F = \frac{Gm_1m_2}{d^2} \text{ dynes,} \tag{1}$$

where

$$G = 6.67 \times 10^{-8},$$

G being the GRAVITATIONAL CONSTANT.

In the case of a small body, such as a man or a space ship, of mass m, on the surface of the earth, equation 1 reduces to

$$\text{force} = F = 980m \text{ dynes (approx.),}$$

and

$$\text{acceleration} = \frac{F}{m} = 980 \text{ cm/sec}^2 \text{ (approx.).}$$

The number 980 is approximately the mean acceleration due to the earth's gravity at the surface of the earth, in cm/sec.^{2} Its exact value is different at different places, being greater at the poles (983 approximately) than at the equator (978 approximately) because d, the radius of the earth, is smaller at the poles (equation 1). A value of 980.112 (correct for Washington, D. C.) is adopted as a standard and called "g."

1

When a man is falling freely near the surface of the earth, his acceleration equals

$$\frac{F}{m} = g.$$

He is then in a field of "1 g." If he is standing on the ground, he is supported by a force of F dynes $= mg$ dynes. He feels a "force of 1 g." In "gravitational units":

$$\text{force} = m \text{ grams.}$$

In the foot-pound system,

$$g = 32.2 \text{ feet/sec}^2,$$

and

$$\text{force due to gravity} = mg \text{ poundals}$$

(where $m =$ mass in pounds). In "gravitational units":

$$\text{force} = m \text{ pounds.}$$

A force of 1 g being a familiar sensation, it is adopted as a standard. For example: a man is in a CENTRIFUGE, being whirled around in a 16-foot radius at a peripheral speed of 64 feet/second. He experiences a centrifugal force:

$$\frac{mv^2}{r} = \frac{(64)^2 m}{16}$$

$$= 256 \, m$$

$$= 8 \times 32 \, m$$

$$= 8 \, mg \text{ (approx).}$$

This is 8 times the force holding up the man's weight when at rest, and he feels a force of 8 g's.

As previously stated, acceleration due to gravity decreases with d according to the inverse square law. This applies to a man in space above the earth's surface. Suppose that he were at a height of about 8000 miles (the earth's diameter) above the earth's surface. Then d would equal 12,000 miles, or 3 times its value at the surface. Thus d^2 would be 9 times greater than at the surface, and the acceleration due to gravity would be 1/9 as great as at the surface, *i.e.*

$$g/9 = \frac{32.2}{9} = 3.58 \text{ feet/sec}^2 \text{ (approx)}$$

$$\text{or } \frac{980}{9} = 108.9 \text{ cms/sec}^2 \text{ (approx).}$$

The man would be in a field of "1/9 of a g." If, instead of accelerating, he were held up in some way, he would feel a force of $\dfrac{mg}{9}$ poundals, *i.e.* $\dfrac{m}{9}$ lbs. That is, he would "weigh" only 1/9 of his usual weight.

Another effect of the earth's gravitational field is the rotation of satellites. In a circular orbit, the gravitational force is equal and opposite to the centrifugal force. In elliptical orbits, the gravitational force varies from PERIGEE to APOGEE, and the satellite obeys a more complicated law. In space flight, a space ship would continuously experience varying gravitational fields. At first the earth's field would predominate; later, that of the moon or of other planets.

On the surface of another planet (or on a moon) the gravitational force —and consequent acceleration—due to gravity differs from that on the surface of the earth. Its value depends on the body's size and density. (The values for the sun, earth's moon, and planets of the solar system in g's are tabulated at the end of this publication.)

The value for a planet may be computed from the planet's mass and radius and "G", the gravitational constant.

For further discussion of space ships in gravitational fields, especially with regard to the passenger's sensations, *see* FREE FALL.

Since the confirmation of Einstein's General Theory of Relativity, physicists have taken a new view of gravitation. To Newton, its discoverer, it was a force of attraction. To Einstein it was a "curvature in space-time." (*See* RELATIVITY.)

accelerometer.   An instrument for measuring acceleration or deceleration. In the simplest form, a small weight is attached by a spring to the frame-

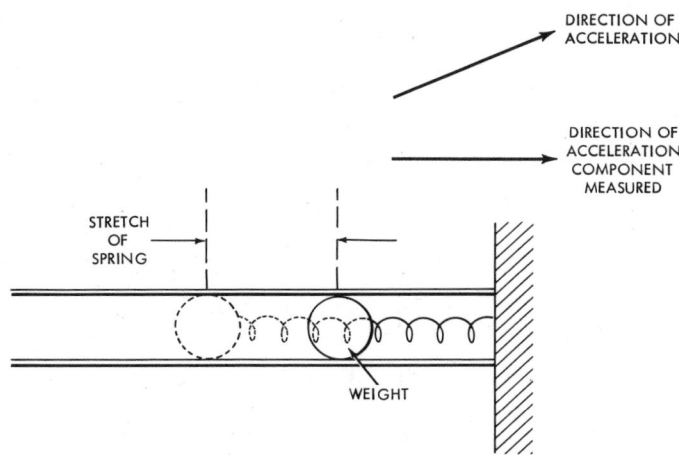

FIG. 1. Principle of the Accelerometer

work of the vehicle whose acceleration is being measured. The weight is constrained to move in a tube or groove in the direction in which acceleration is being measured. If there is acceleration in some other direction, the accelerometer will measure only its component parallel to the tube or groove. Figure 1 illustrates the mechanical principle of this type of accelerometer. Other types are based on the pendulum and gyroscope.

active homing. *See under* HOMING.

Aerobee. An unguided high-altitude rocket developed in the period between the development of the VIKING and that of the WAC CORPORAL. It is launched from a tiltable, 140-foot high, launching tower. A solid-propellant booster is used to obtain a speed high enough to stabilize the missile before it leaves the launcher. The main power unit uses liquid propellant. Length: 19 feet. Diameter: 15 inches. Payload: 150 pounds. Range: about 150 miles. Maximum acceleration: 12 g, at take-off.

aerodynamics. The branch of physical science concerned with the reactions caused by relative motion between a solid body and the surrounding air.

aeroelasticity. The branch of physical science concerned with the mutual interaction of elastic forces with aerodynamic and inertial forces in an aircraft or missile structure. Static aeroelasticity deals with the interaction of only elastic and AERODYNAMIC forces, *e.g.* such problems as load distribution on a flexible wing. Dynamic aeroelasticity deals with elastic, aerodynamic, and inertial forces, *e.g.* such problems as FLUTTER or autopilot installations on flexible surfaces.

aeroembolism. Sickness caused by the escape of dissolved nitrogen from the blood in the form of bubbles when at high altitudes without wearing a PRESSURE SUIT. Astronaut's equivalent of the "bends."

aeropause. An altitude marking the practical limit above which there are no aerodynamic effects due to atmosphere. "Beyond the aeropause the atmosphere ceases" expresses the idea in popular terms. As so defined, the term is loose, having different interpretations according to the type of aerodynamic effects under consideration. For instance, 20 miles (approximate) represents the upper limit of jet flight; 250 to 300 miles represents the upper limit for satellite ORBITAL DECAY due to DRAG.

aero-space. Air Force designation for the region comprised of earth's atmosphere and all outer space.

aerothermoelasticity. The branch of physical science concerned with AEROELASTICITY with the additional factor of aerodynamic heating. A BOOST-GLIDE vehicle in hypersonic flight presents typical problems of aerothermoelasticity.

AEW.   Airborne early warning.

AFBMD.   Air Force Ballistic Missile Division.

AFMTC.   Air Force Missile Test Center.

AFSWC.   Air Force Special Weapons Center.

after-burning.   *1.* The irregular burning of certain rocket motors after the main burning and thrust have ceased. (*See also* Engine, rocket.)
    2. Fuel injection and combustion in a turbojet exhaust vent.

AGM.   Air-to-ground missile.

AICBM.   Anti-intercontinental ballistic missile.

ailavator.   A control surface on a missile performing the same functions as an elevator and aileron on an aircraft. On a spinning missile, these functions are constantly interchanged. Owing to the high speed of missiles, ailavators are proportionately much smaller than elevators and ailerons.

air break-up.   The willful fragmentation of a missile in the air in order to increase air resistance during its return to earth. This reduces impact force and increases chances of successful instrument recovery.

air breather.   An aircraft or missile of the piston engine or jet-propulsion type, requiring ambient air for final combustion; as distinct from rockets, which contain reagents for their fuel and can function in a vacuum.

aircraft rocket.   A rocket launched from an aircraft.

airfoil.   A body whose shape causes it to receive a useful reaction from an air stream moving relative to it. The term is usually associated with wing-like or fin-like structures. Two air-foil classification systems have been devised, *viz.* a 4-digit and a 5-digit system.
    The NACA 4-digit system describes: 1) the maximum camber of the mean line, 2) its position on the chord, 3) and 4) the maximum thickness. The 5-digit system similarly employs a combination of numbers of describe camber line and thickness.

Air Force Ballistic Missile Division.   A division of Headquarters Air Research and Development command. Responsible for the development of an operational intercontinental ballistic missile.

Air Force Missile Test Center.   A major subdivision of Air Research and Development Command. Responsible for the missile launching site at Cape Canaveral.

Air Force Special Weapons Center.   An Air Research and Development Command center. Responsible for developing and testing atomic weapons, their systems, components, and personnel hazards associated with their employment.

air-launched ballistic missile. BALLISTIC MISSILE launched from an airbound platform such as a B-52 bomber. A range of about 1000 miles is planned.

air lock. An air-tight compartment in which the air pressure may be regulated to any desired value. In SPACE FLIGHT, air locks permit the passage of personnel from the interior of the ship (at normal pressure) to the outside (at zero pressure). An air lock must have two airtight doors, one leading to the interior of the ship and one to the outside, and valves for admitting and releasing air. In leaving the ship, passengers (wearing PRESSURE SUITS) would enter the air lock, after which the door leading to the interior would be closed. The door to the outside would be opened.

Air Research and Development Command. A major command of the Air Force. Responsible for carrying out research and development in basic and applied science and in human engineering, in order to provide for Air Force requirements.

air resistance. *See* DRAG.

ALBM. Air launched ballistic missile.

AME. Angle-measuring equipment.

AMM. ANTI-MISSILE MISSILE. Also called "Auntie."

anoxia. A condition of insufficient aeration of the blood or lack of oxygen in the body.

antigravity. The long-sought-for but still hypothetical cancellation of the gravitational field. (*See* ELECTROGRAVITICS and SPACE FLIGHT.)

antimatter. A substance believed to be constituted in the reverse manner from matter; *i.e.*, the atomic nuclei are negative and the electrons are positive. When matter and antimatter are brought together, there is a reaction, and both are converted into energy. Antiparticles have been made in the laboratory but have not been found in nature.

anti-missile missile. *See under* MISSILE.

aphelion. The point in a planet's orbit around the sun where it is farthest from the sun.

apogee. The point in a satellite's orbit around the earth where it is farthest from the earth. (*See* figure 2.) The term is also applied to ballistic missiles, where it signifies the highest point in the trajectory.

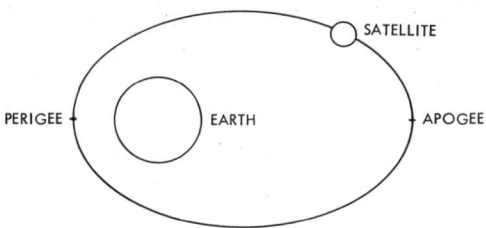

Fig. 2.   Apogee and Perigee

Appleton layer.   F-layer of the IONOSPHERE.

ARCAS.   Single-stage meterological SOUNDING ROCKET. Solid propellant. Fired from a closed-breech launcher. Peak altitude: 206,000 feet. Payload: 12 pounds.

ARCON.   Navy rocket for upper-air research. Designed to carry a 40-pound payload to about 70 miles, or a 10-pound payload to about 100 miles. Length; 12 feet.

ARDC.   Air Research and Development Command.

aerology.   "Geography" of Mars.

Army Ballistic Missile Agency.   Army office responsible for research and development of rocket missiles and vehicles.

ARPA.   Advanced Research Projects Agency.

ARS.   1. American Rocket Society.
   2. Advanced RECONNAISSANCE SATELLITE. (*See* PIED PIPER.)

artificial gravity.   The simulation of gravity by centrifugal force. Probably to be used for space stations and, less probably, space ships. A space station will be rotated by an initial rocket thrust (discontinued) at such a rate that

$$T = 2\pi \sqrt{\frac{r}{ng}},$$

where

T = period of rotation in seconds,
r = radius of rotation in feet,
n = number of g's that it is desired to simulate, and
g = 32.2.

artificial moon.   Man-made moon.   *See* SATELLITE, ARTIFICIAL.

artificial planet.   SUN SATELLITE.

artificial satellite.   *See* SATELLITE, ARTIFICIAL.

ASM.   Air-to-surface missile.

ASROC. Anti-Submarine Rocket, or—some say—Atomic Submarine Rocket. Launched underwater, the ASROC covers most of its distance through the air, re-entering the water to seek its target by acoustical homing.

ASTOR. Anti-Submarine Torpedo Ordnance Rocket. ASTOR is based on a vehicle the size of a Mark 18 torpedo. A nuclear warhead gives it a large "kill" radius when used. It is one of several such underwater atomic weapons being developed by the Navy for use against supersubmarines.

astrobiology. The branch of biology concerned with plant and animal life on planets other than earth.

Astrodyne. Type of ROCKET SLED.

ASTRON. A project which will use a cylinder of rotating electrons, moving at speeds approaching that of light, to produce "plasma pinch." (*See* PLASMA.) An electron gun of several million electron volts energy will shoot the plasma beam into a vacuum chamber containing deuterium. A sheath of extremely high-speed electrons will both heat and confine the plasma.

astronautics. The science of SPACE FLIGHT. Astronaut.

athodyd. Aerothermodynamic duct. A form of RAMJET frequently referred to as "the flying stove-pipe." It consists simply of a long tube with open ends slightly restricted, and its thrust is the result of continuous burning of fuel within the tube. (*See* figure 3.) The athodyd requires an initial source of propulsion to attain the velocity required for starting.

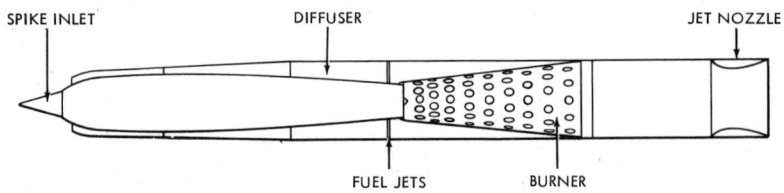

SPIKE INLET   DIFFUSER   JET NOZZLE

FUEL JETS   BURNER

FIG. 3. Athodyd Ramjet (Van Nostrand's Scientific Encyclopedia, D. Van Nostrand Company, Inc.)

Atlas. Air Force surface-to-surface high-accuracy ICBM. Doppler radar command guidance during the powered first portion of the flight. It uses two-stage liquid fuel engines, approximately 300,000 pounds thrust for the first stage. Range: up to 6500 miles. Speed: 15,000 mph (maximum). Inertial guidance systems are now being developed. An Atlas missile was placed in orbit around the earth on 18 December 1958. *See* SATELITE, ARTIFICIAL and PROJECT SCORE.

atmosphere. The blanket of air surrounding the earth, necessary for the operation of all aircraft and missiles, excepting rockets. "Normal" atmospheric pressure of 15 pounds per square inch exists at the surface (sea level) of the earth. At greater heights, atmospheric pressure progressively falls off. The atmosphere is conventionally divided into the following layers. (figure 4):

1. Troposphere (between ground and 10 miles altitude)
2. Stratosphere (between 10 and 16 miles altitude)
3. Mesosphere (or chemosphere) (between 16 and 50 miles altitude[1])
4. Ionosphere (varying between 40 and 50 and 175 to 250 miles altitude)
5. Thermosphere (between 50 and 300 miles altitude)
6. Exosphere (between 300 and 1000 miles altitude)

The upper and lower limits are those generally considered acceptable. They are approximate, and vary with weather conditions, time of year, and latitude.

For more detailed data, *see* TROPOSPHERE, STRATOSPHERE, etc.

atomic energy. Energy latent in the nucleus of an atom. This energy is liberated when nuclei combine to form a new nucleus (fusion) or break up to form new nuclei (fission). In both fusion and fission, a portion of nuclear matter is converted to energy according to the relativistic equation $E = mc^2$, where c is the velocity of light (3×10^{10} cm/sec). The rate of exchange of mass into energy is approximately 10^{21} ergs per gram. The A-bomb operates by fission, the H-bomb by fusion. When atomic energy is released quickly, as in a bomb, it manifests itself as heat, shock wave, sound wave, neutron impact, atomic impact, and high-frequency radiation. These phenomena are all destructive, the most lasting being "fallout," *i.e.* radiation from materials made radioactive at the explosion.

When atomic energy is controlled so as to be liberated slowly, and anti-radiation shielding is provided, the heat energy may be used to operate atomic motors. It is hoped that atomic energy may eventually be controlled according to some principle not involving heat. (*See also* ATOMIC FUEL and REACTOR, NUCLEAR.)

atomic fission. *See* FISSION, NUCLEAR.

atomic fuel. Fuel, envisaged for future rockets, which would power a vehicle by the release of ATOMIC ENERGY, not by chemical combustion. It is hoped that eventually atomic energy will be harnessed according to some new principle not involving heat. Then it may be possible to produce ultra-high exhaust velocities for the products of atomic fission or fusion, possibly of the order of 3×10^9 cm/sec, *i.e.* SPECIFIC IMPULSES of the order of 3 million. Very high rocket velocities would then be possible with a MASS RATIO scarcely exceeding 1.

---

[1] According to Chapman. According to Wares, however, the mesosphere lies between 250 and 600 miles altitude.

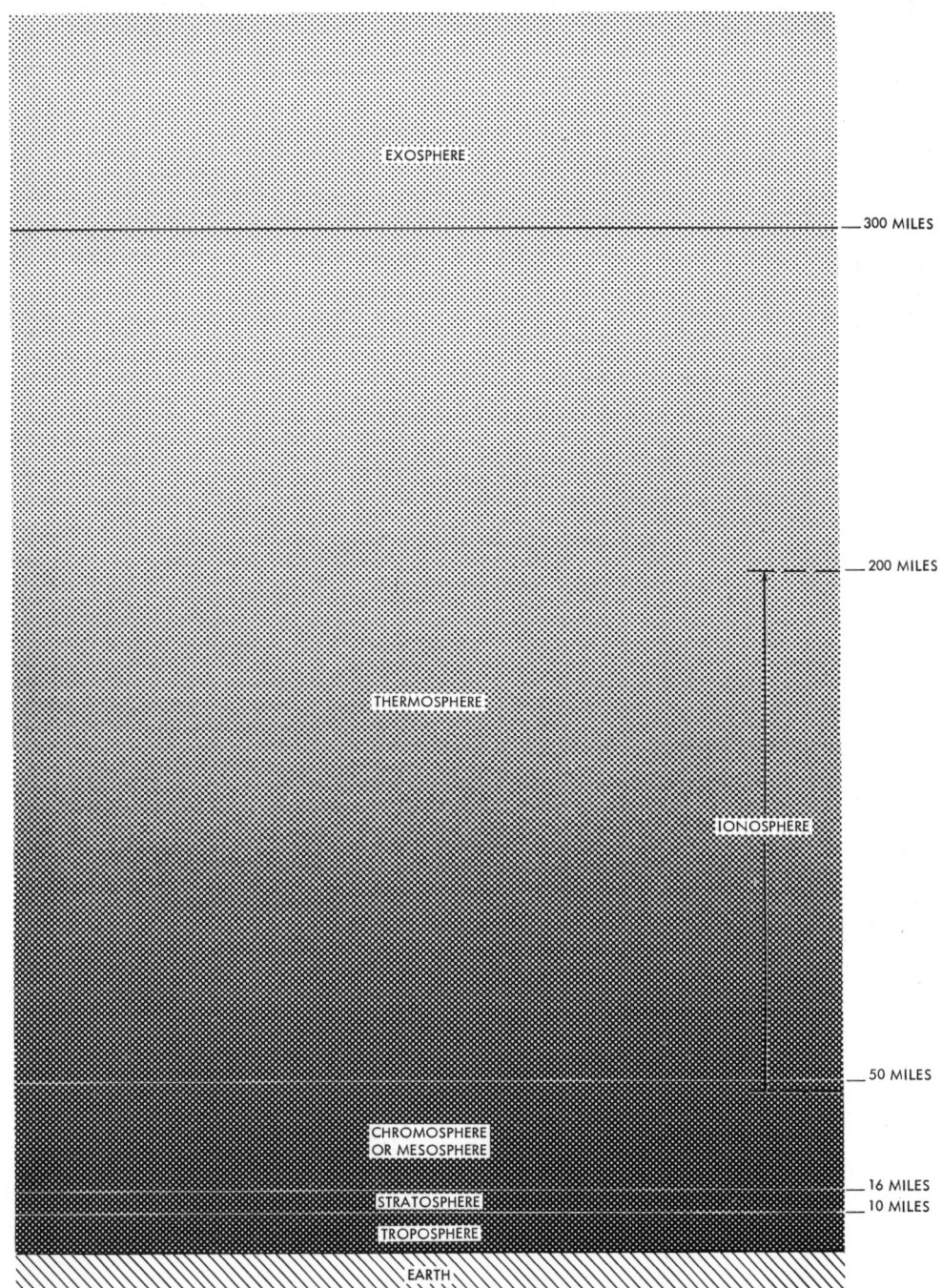

EXOSPHERE

_____ 300 MILES

_____ 200 MILES

THERMOSPHERE

IONOSPHERE

_____ 50 MILES

CHROMOSPHERE
OR MESOSPHERE

_____ 16 MILES
STRATOSPHERE
_____ 10 MILES
TROPOSPHERE
EARTH

Fig. 4. Layers of the Atmosphere

atomic fusion.   *See* FUSION, NUCLEAR.

atomic motor.   A motor obtaining its primal energy from controlled ATOMIC ENERGY. A simple example is a motor which converts atomic energy to the heat that operates a steam engine. Another example is a device which converts atomic energy to the electrical energy that charges a battery.

atomic pile.   *See* REACTOR, NUCLEAR.

ATRAN.   A map-matching navigation system, which permits extremely low-level penetration.

ATS.   Air-to-ship.

attitude.   The position of the principle axes of an aerodynamic vehicle with respect to the true vertical or to an arbitrary but defined frame of reference.

AUM.   Air-to-underwater missile.

Auntie.   ANTI-MISSILE MISSILE. *Colloq.*

B

B-52 Defense.   Air Force air-to-air B-52 aircraft defense missile.

back-out.   Reversal of a COUNT-DOWN procedure in order to postpone the launching of a missile or vehicle.

Baka.   Japanese rocket-assisted aircraft. Designed for Kamikaze attack (suicide mission). It is launched by a mother aircraft. Solid propellant.

ballistic missile.   *See under* MISSILE.

Ballistic Missile Office.   Office of Headquarters Air Material Command. Designed to provide a streamlined logistics system for IRBM's and ICBM's. Established at Inglewood, Cal.

balloon.   A lighter-than-air vehicle used to explore the atmosphere. It may be captive or free. (*See also* ROCKOON.)

Bat.   Army rocket. One of first two U.S.A. operational missiles. Used in World War II.

bazooka.   Anti-tank rocket, first used in World War II. Fires a shaped charge. Fin-stabilized. Length: 18 inches. Weight: 33 pounds.

beam.   A volume of directed radiant energy.

beam guidance.   *See under* GUIDANCE, MISSILE.

beam-rider guidance.   BEAM GUIDANCE.

Big Brother. Nickname of Air Force Weapon System WS-117L project (derived from the project's role of surveillance). The DISCOVERER program is one of its offshoots.

bioastronautics. *See* SPACE MEDICINE.

biosatellite. A satellite supporting plant and animal life.

bipropellant. *See under* PROPELLANT.

bird. GUIDED MISSILE. *Colloq.*

blackout. A temporary loss of vision and/or consciousness when subjected to high acceleration forces.

blast-off. The instant of occurrence of the initial explosion that launches a rocket missile from its launch pad.

blast shield. A shaped, protective material that deflects blast, or otherwise protects personnel or equipment when a rocket is fired.

blindness, space. *See* SPACE MEDICINE.

blockhouse. A protective shelter near one or more launch pads containing missile control and monitoring equipment and operating personnel.

blood-boiling. A fatal consequence of subjecting the body to extremely low ambient pressures, causing rapid evaporation of the blood and other body fluids. The reduction of pressure due to space ship leaks or space suit or air lock failure is one of the greatest hazards of space flight.

Bloodhound. British surface-to-air medium-range guided missile ramjet. Semi-active homer with rocket boosters. Speed: Mach 2-2.5.

Blue Streak. Proposed British IRBM. Adaptable for launching LUNAR PROBES. Range: 2000-2500 miles.

BMD. Ballistic Missile Division (Air Force).

BMEWS. Ballistic missile early warning system.

BMO. BALLISTIC MISSILE OFFICE.

boil-off. Vaporization of a cold liquid propellant. Boil-off is caused by rising temperature due to exposure to local weather conditions through the walls of the missile fuel tank or other non-insulated containers.

Bold Orion. Air Force air-to-surface missile. May be part of the development programs for WS-138A.

Bomarc. Air Force surface-to-air missile with radar command guidance. Uses a solid- or liquid-propellant rocket booster and two ramjet engines. Range: over 200-250 miles. Speed: Mach 2-5.

boost glide. A type of flight in which a missile or aircraft is powered only during the initial portion of flight and then glides through the atmosphere to its destination (figure 5).

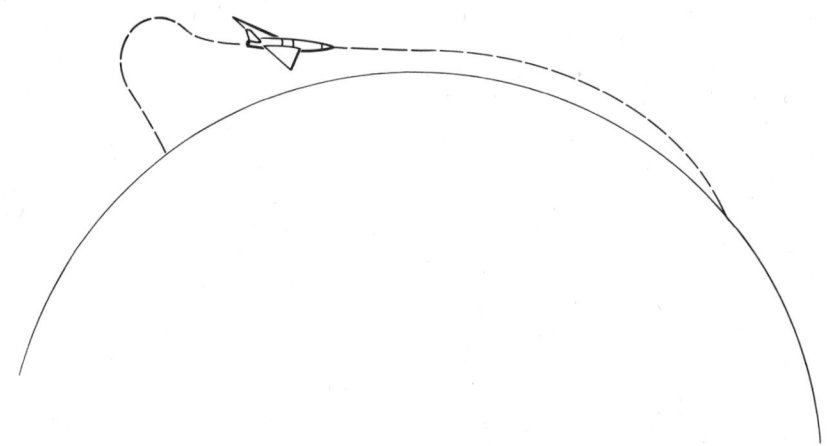

Fɪɢ. 5.   Boost-glide Path

booster. An auxiliary rocket engine generally used to bring a missile up to a required velocity. The booster is usually separated and dropped after ʙᴜʀɴᴏᴜᴛ. A booster may contain one or more stages.

brain. Guidance system of a missile. *Colloq.*

brake rocket. A ʀᴇᴛʀᴏʀᴏᴄᴋᴇᴛ.

braking orbit. *See* Oʀʙɪᴛ, ʙʀᴀᴋɪɴɢ.

Brennschluss. *See* Bᴜʀɴᴏᴜᴛ.

Bulldog. Navy hypersonic air-to-ground missile. A larger version of the Bᴜʟʟᴘᴜᴘ.

Bullpup. Navy hypersonic air-to-ground missile. Guided by aircraft command. Solid propellant. Can carry 250-pound warhead.

bunkerscope. A viewing device that permits observation and photography, from a blockhouse, of hazardous processes such as missile firing and static testing.

burnout. Also known as "Brennschluss." The instant that the engines of a rocket missile cease to fire, and the missile goes into a free, unpowered trajectory.

—burnout velocity. The velocity of a rocket at burnout.

burn-up. *1.* The vaporization of a rocket or artificial satellite due to atmospheric friction.

2. The fissioning of nuclear fuel. (*See* FISSION, NUCLEAR.)

C

c. The symbol for the constant equal to the VELOCITY OF LIGHT in cms/sec (2.9977×10^{10}).

capsule. *See under* specific type.

carrier rocket. A ferry vehicle. *See under* ROCKET.

captive firing. *See* STATIC FIRING and STATIC TESTING.

captive test. *See* STATIC FIRING and STATIC TESTING.

celestial-navigation guidance. *See under* GUIDANCE, MISSILE.

Centaur. One of a new, projected family of rockets designed to put a 730-pound payload on the moon, carry instruments to Mars and Venus, or put a 7400-pound satellite into a 300-mile orbit. Will use an ATLAS-type first stage and a specially designed hydrogen-burning second stage. The third stage will be a new rocket, carrying a fuel which will be ignited in outer space.

centrifuge. A mechanical device using centrifugal force to produce simulated high gravitational fields on bodies, animate or inanimate, by rotating them in a circular path at a constant speed. Fields of very many g's are used to test materials or to separate out solid constituents in liquids. Fields of 5 to 20 or (more rarely) more g's are used to test the reactions of animals and human beings to accelerations likely to be encountered in space flight (figure 6). The principle of the centrifuge will probably be used to simulate gravity in SPACE STATIONS, which will be rotated at such a frequency as to produce a centrifiugal force of 1 g (or possibly less). *See* ACCELERATION DUE TO GRAVITY.

CH-17. USSR missile. *See* COMET 1.

CH-18. USSR missile. *See* COMET 2.

chaff. *See* WINDOW.

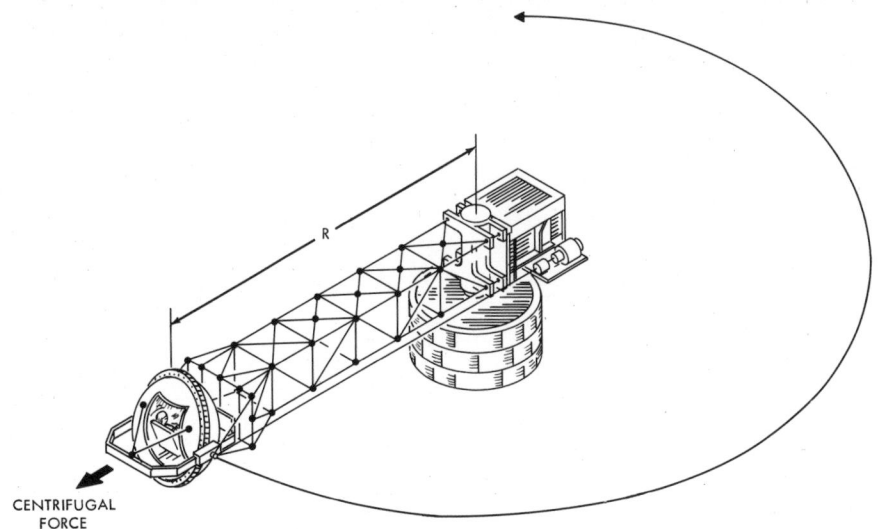

CENTRIFUGAL
FORCE

Fɪɢ. 6. Centrifuge

chemosphere. *See* Mᴇsᴏᴘʜᴇʀᴇ.

chugging. *See* Rᴇsᴏɴᴀɴᴛ ʙᴜʀɴɪɴɢ.

circumlunar rocket. *See under* Rᴏᴄᴋᴇᴛ.

cislunar. Pertaining to a sphere centered on the earth with a radius equal to the distance to the moon.

clock paradox. *See* Tɪᴍᴇ ᴅɪʟᴀᴛɪᴏɴ.

coasting. The movement of a rocket or missile when it is not in powered flight.

collision course. A path of a missile anticipating the motion of the target and directed not toward but ahead of the target's present position. This path may or may not be straight line, *i.e.* a "ᴄᴏɴsᴛᴀɴᴛ-ʙᴇᴀʀɪɴɢ ᴄᴏᴜʀsᴇ."

collision-course guidance. *See under* Gᴜɪᴅᴀɴᴄᴇ, ᴍɪssɪʟᴇ.

combustion chamber. The area inside a jet or rocket where the combustion of fuel takes place, the expansion of combustion products through the exhaust nozzle providing the forward thrust. The ingredients of combustion are all contained within the rocket and are injected into the combustion chamber when the moment has come to operate it. In athodyd-type ʀᴀᴍ-ᴊᴇᴛs, the fuel is injected into the chamber and mixed with air admitted through the front nozzle. In pulse-type ramjets, the air is admitted through a valve. In ᴛᴜʀʙᴏᴊᴇᴛs, the air is admitted through a compressor, operated by a turbine driven by the expansion of the combustion products. In rockets, no air is admitted.

Comet 1. USSR surface-to-surface single-stage rocket missile. Solid propellant. Burning time: 18 seconds. Maximum ceiling: about 42 miles. Thrust-to-weight ratio: 2.63. (Also designated CH-17.)

Comet 2. USSR surface-to-surface single-stage rocket missile. Solid propellant. Burning time: 115 seconds. Peak height: 195 miles. Thrust-to-weight ratio: 2.4. Warhead is larger than in Comet 1. (Also designated CH-18.)

command guidance. *See under* GUIDANCE, MISSILE.

confusion reflector. A reflector of electromagnetic radiation used to create echoes for confusion purposes against radars, guided missiles, and proximity fuzes. WINDOW is an example.

constant-bearing course. A COLLISION COURSE in which the missile flies toward the target in a path that approximates a straight line for short distances; strictly speaking, the path is a great circle.

constant-bearing course guidance. *See under* GUIDANCE, MISSILE.

controlled fusion. *See* PLASMA PINCH.

Corporal. Army ballistic missile. Liquid propellant. Range: 75 miles. Diameter: 30 inches. Length: 46 feet. Nose cone length: 8 feet. To be replaced by the SERGEANT.

Corvus. Navy and Marine Corps air-to-surface missile.

cosmic dust. Clouds of obscuring particles in interstellar space.

cosmic rays. Extremely high-frequency radiation set up by the bombardment of sub-atomic particles believed to originate in the sun and other stars.

COTAR. Correlation tracking system. It is a combination of two AME's.

count-down. The period immediately preceding the launching of a missile during which various components are checked and made ready for launching. It terminates with the command "9-8-7-6-5-4-3-2-1-FIRE!"

Crossbow. Navy air-to-surface turbojet missile. Homes on enemy radar. Speed: about 500 knots.

cruciform configuration. A configuration in which the aerodynamic control surfaces of a missile are identical and symmetrically located at right angles to each other around the missile body.

D

Dart. Army surface-to-surface wire-guided anti-tank missile. Smokeless rocket propellant.

data capsule. RECOVERY PACKAGE.

dawn rocket. *See under* ROCKET.

decoy missile. Diversionary missile. *See under* MISSILE.

Diamond Back. Navy air-to-air guided missile. Uses infrared homing. May use liquid-packaged propellant. Successor to the SIDEWINDER.

diergolic propellant. *See under* PROPELLANT.

diffuser. A duct of varying cross-section that converts high-speed gas flow into low-speed flow at increased pressure.

Discoverer. A class of artificial satellites. *See* SATELLITE, ARTIFICIAL.

dish. The reflective portion of a parabolic antenna. *Colloq.*

DME. Distance-measuring equipment.

Doppler effect. The apparent change in the frequency of a radiated wave when there is relative motion between the source and the observer.

Doppler guidance. *See under* GUIDANCE, MISSILE.

Doppler radar guidance. *See under* GUIDANCE, MISSILE.

DORAN. Doppler ranging. A system using phase comparison to determine missile range. Similar to DOVAP.

DOVAP. A form of DOPPLER GUIDANCE.

Dove. Navy air-to-surface rocket missile. Solid propellant.

down range. Any area along the flight course of a missile. Down-range tracking stations report on missile flight behavior and receive telemetered data from the missile.

drag. The force opposite to the direction of motion exerted on a missile by the medium through which it is passing. Drag is proportional to the cross-sectional area of an object of given shape normal to its direction of motion. Drag also depends on the shape and velocity of the object. It increases with velocity in accordance with a complicated mathematical function.

drag chute. A parachute of the type used to slow down aircraft on a runway, now proposed to slow down a RE-ENTRY VEHICLE, such as a manned satellite, space capsule, or ICBM nose cone, during re-entry into the earth's atmosphere. It would not be released until the vehicle had been sufficiently slowed down by other means, such as RETROROCKETS.

drag, ram. A quantity defining the drag induced by the air required for combustion in a jet engine. It equals the product of mass flow and airspeed divided by g (the acceleration of gravity).

drone. A remotely controlled, pilotless aircraft.

Duck. Air Force air-to-air missile.

dusk rocket. *See under* ROCKET.

dynamic instability. *See* SONANCE.

dynamic pressure. Pressure on a moving body due to the barometric pressure of the ambient atmosphere and to motion through that atmosphere. Dynamic pressure increases with velocity.

dynamic stability. *See* STABILITY, DYNAMIC.

Dyna-Soar. Air Force surface-to-surface manned vehicle. It is rocket-boosted to an altitude of 100-150 miles and then glides to its destination assisted by small sustainer rockets. Range: 12,000-25,000 miles.

dysbarism. Decompression sickness.

E

Eagle. Navy air-to-ground and air-to-air missile. Range: 50-100 miles.

earth. Home of mankind and third planet of the solar system.

earth satellite. An ARTIFICIAL SATELLITE orbiting the earth.

ebullism. The formation of water vapor bubbles in the tissues brought on by blood-boiling.

E layer. *See* IONOSPHERE.

electrogravitics. The hoped-for science of controlling or neutralizing gravitational fields, or creating new ones. Doubts have been expressed whether such a revolutionary discovery can be made without the prior discovery of a new fundamental principle in science. It has been pointed out that such discoveries are usually made accidentally in the course of basic research, not "to order." Yet several universities and other learned bodies in the U.S.A. are reported to be investigating this subject. (*See also* SPACE FLIGHT.)

elevon.   *See* AILAVATOR.

ELSEE.   Electronic sky screen.

end burner.   Restricted propellant. *See under* PROPELLANT.

energy, atomic.   *See* ATOMIC ENERGY.

engine, jet.   *See* JET.

engine, rocket.   The portion of a rocket which provides the thrust, by means of fuel combustion and expansion of the combustion products through the exhaust nozzle. At burnout, the engine housing is expended. (*See also* ROCKET.)

erector.   Missile-handling equipment used to position missiles for vertical launching.

escape capsule.   An enclosed compartment providing a protective environment for a safe human ejection from high-speed, high-altitude aircraft. The escape capsule contains parachutes and/or other means for safe descent.

escape velocity.   The minimum velocity which a body must have at the initial point of a ballistic path in order for the gravitational field acting on the body to cause the body to describe a parabolic or hyperbolic orbit instead of an elliptical one. When this condition is realized, the body will not return to the initial point and is said to have "escaped."

The most familiar example of this is a space vehicle powered by a rocket. At the instant of BURNOUT, the ballistic path begins; at that instant, the vehicle's velocity must exceed the value of escape velocity *at that point*. This velocity is a function of the earth's gravity and the vehicle's altitude. The direction of motion (if above horizontal) is immaterial. Escape velocity decreases as altitude increases. For escape from the earth, the velocity is given by the equation

$$\text{escape velocity} = \sqrt{2g'R'},$$

where

$g' =$ acceleration due to gravity at the initial point of the ballistic path,

and

$R' =$ distance of the initial point from the center of the earth.

If $h =$ the altitude of the initial point in miles, the n$R' = 400 + h$. This, approximately, reduces to:

$$\text{escape velocity} = 7 \sqrt{\frac{4000}{4000 + h}} \text{ miles/sec.}$$

Escape velocity at any point equals $\sqrt{2} \times$ orbital velocity (for a circular orbit) at that point. (*See* ORBITS, CIRCULAR, MECHANICS OF.)

If the body is projected at exactly escape velocity, its path is parabolic; for all higher velocities, hyperbolic. Figure 7 shows:

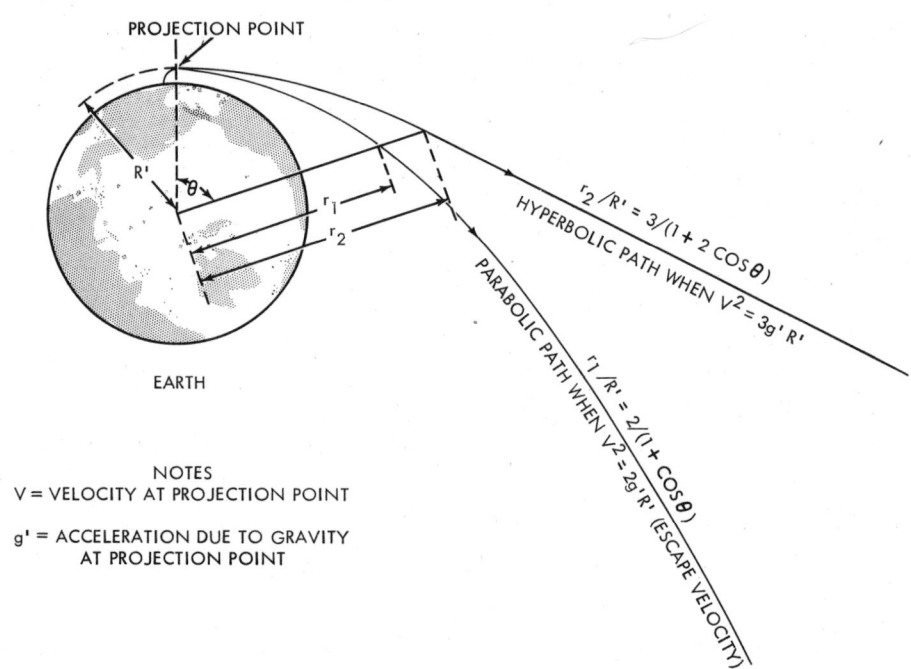

FIG. 7.   Parabolic and Hyperbolic Paths of an Escaped Ballistic Body

1. The parabolic path of a body projected horizontally at exactly escape velocity, such that:

$$V^2 = 2g'R'.$$

At 400 miles altitude, V equals about 6.6 miles/second. The polar equation of the path is

$$\frac{r_1}{R'} = \frac{2}{1 + \cos \theta},$$

where r_1 = radius vector

          θ = angle between radius vector and line to projection point.

2. The hyperbolic path of a body projected horizontally from the same point at a slightly greater velocity, such that

$$V^2 = 3g'R'.$$

At 400 miles altitude, V equals about 8.1 miles/second. The polar equation of the path is

$$\frac{r_2}{R'} = \frac{3}{1 + 2 \cos \theta},$$

where

$$r_2 = \text{radius vector.}$$

Escape velocity also depends on the radius and density of the planet or moon from which the missile is escaping. For the moon it would be less, for Jupiter greater than for the earth (considering escape velocity at the surface).

EX-8. Navy underwater anti-submarine rocket or hydroduct powered torpedo. Speed: possibly exceeding 150 knots. Reportedly, a new method of cavitation control decreases drag and noise.

exhaust.   The combination products that leave a rocket combustion chamber.

exhaust velocity.   The velocity at which the discharged gases escape from the outlet nozzle, relative to the rocket. It is a measure of the rocket's merit. (*See* Impulse, specific.)

exosphere.   The layer of the atmosphere between 300 and 1000 miles above the surface of the earth. An earth satellite should have its perigee within or above this region in order to be completely free from atmospheric drag leading to orbital decay.

exotic fuel.   Rocket fuel differing from the conventional hydrocarbon fuels such as kerosene, gasoline, etc. Eamples:
    1. Hydrides of light metals such as boron or lithium.
    2. Magnesium or aluminum powder suspended in hydrocarbon fuel.
    3. Atomic fuels.
Exotic fuels are expected to achieve higher exhaust velocities than conventional fuels, thereby reducing mass ratio. (*See also* Propellant.)

Explorer.   A class of artifical satellites. *See* Satellite, artificial.

explosive bolt.   A securing assembly containing a shaped, explosive charge or a loaded spring that can be set off electrically to provide positive release of items secured. This type of device is frequently used in positive separation of rocket stages while the missile is in flight.

F

Falcon. Class of Air Force air-to-air guided missiles. Solid propellant. Thrust: 6000 pounds. Range: approximately 5 miles. Speed: Mach 2+. Models differ only in means of guidance.

—*Falcon I.* A radar-guided missile.

—*Falcon II.* An infrared homing missile.

fallout. Radiation from materials made radioactive by a nuclear explosion. (*See* ATOMIC ENERGY.)

Farside. *See* OPERATION FARSIDE and PROJECT FARSIDE.

ferry rocket. *See under* ROCKET.

Fireflash. British air-to-air guided missile. Beam-rider guidance. Unpowered except for two solid-propellant boosters which break away. Length: 7½ feet. Has CRUCIFORM wings. Beam-controlled by gyro gunsight.

Firestreak. British air-to-air guided missile. Passive infrared homing missile with internal solid-propellant rocket power plant. Speed: Mach 2.5-3. Length: 10½ feet.

fission, nuclear. The release of ATOMIC ENERGY due to the splitting of an atom, thereby forming two or more atoms of different elements. Some of the matter in the original atom is converted into energy.

Fitzgerald contraction. *See* TIME DILATATION.

fixed satellite. *See under* SATELLITE, ARTIFICIAL.

F layer. *See* IONOSPHERE.

flight. 1. The smallest Air Force missile organization possessing both launching and guidance capability.
    2. The path of an aircraft or guided missile.

flutter. Oscillation of definite period but unstable character set up in any part of an aircraft or missile by a momentary disturbance, and maintained by a combination of aerodynamic, inertial, and elastic characteristics of the aircraft. The term is also used to describe certain distortions encountered in communications, recording, and reproducing.

flying saucer. An unidentified flying object. *Colloq.*

free ascent. *See* COASTING.

free fall. A body is said to be in free fall if it is not resisting the gravitational field in which it is situated. (This field may be due to several at-

tracting bodies: sun, planet, moon, etc.) That is to say, it is not being supported by ground or sea, or being subjected to friction by ground or sea
or atmosphere, or being accelerated or decelerated by rocket thrust. It is
moving in accordance with the gravitational field according to the law: acceleration = force divided by mass. The acceleration is in the direction of
the field. If the body has an initial velocity not due to the field, its velocity
at any moment is the resultant of that original velocity and the velocity
caused by the field (field × time field has acted, if the field is uniform).

Figure 8 shows three stages of a body moving in a uniform gravitational
field. Stage 1 shows the initial velocity as a vector at time zero. The velocity
caused by the field = zero. Stage 2 shows the initial velocity, velocity due
to a constant, oblique field, and resultant velocity after a short time. Stage

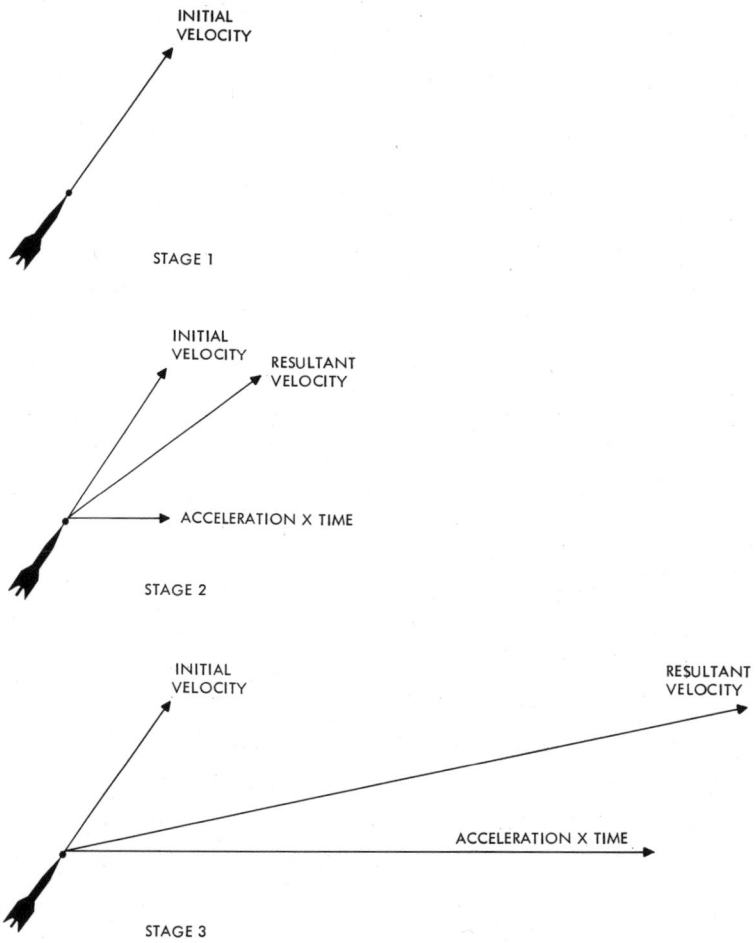

FIG. 8.   Growth of Velocity with Oblique Forward Acceleration

3 shows the three velocities after a long time. Note that the orientation of the body does not change, but merely its direction of motion.

If the initial velocity is opposed to the field, the resultant velocity will also be opposed to the field until the field velocity has grown large enough to equal the initial velocity. During this time, the acceleration appears as a deceleration in the resultant velocity opposed to the field. Example: a stone thrown upward, before it begins to fall. It is as much in free fall while rising as while falling. Figure 9 shows the three stages when the

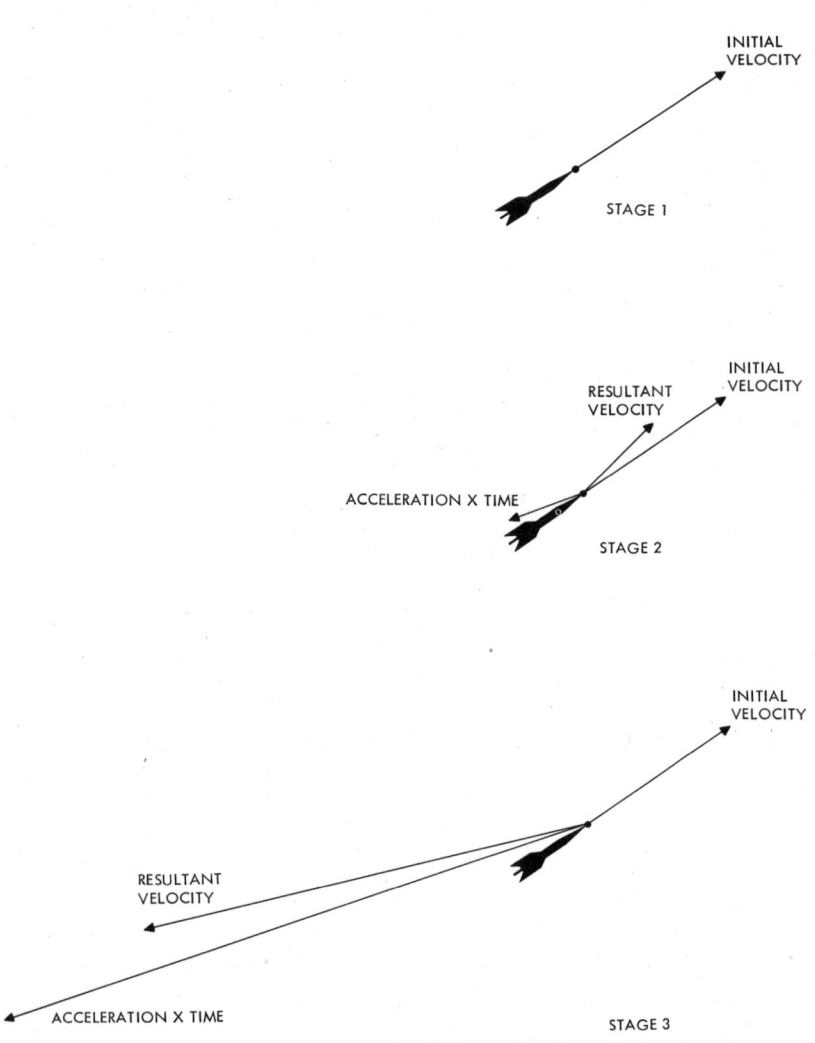

FIG. 9. Growth of Velocity with Oblique Backward Acceleration

field is in almost the opposite direction to the initial velocity, after a short and after a long time.

In the absence of a gravitational field (a condition almost realized far out in space), a body is in free fall if it is at rest or traveling with a constant velocity in a straight line.

Free fall is *perfectly* realized only in vacuum.

A passenger inside a vehicle which is in free fall feels "weightless." This is because the vehicle is not resisting the field and so is not supporting the passenger. Vehicle and passenger are freely accelerating together, in accordance with the action of the field. No force is being exerted by the floor of the vehicle on the passenger's feet. There is no force between his feet and the rest of his body. His arm held outward does not fall. Nothing in the vehicle falls *relative to the* vehicle. The sensation of weightlessness is similar to that experienced (almost) on earth when falling. Thus the passenger would feel as if he and the vehicle were falling, because of the absence of the familiar forces within his body which resistance to gravity causes on the earth.

Examples of free fall:

1. Falling through a vacuum.

2. Rising through a vacuum just after being fired from a gun.

3. COASTING through space.

4. An artificial satellite in orbit. If the orbit is circular, centrifugal force balances gravitational force at all points of the orbit. Both forces act equally on vehicle and passenger.

5. Resting or coasting at uniform speed in a straight line in distant space (not in a gravitational field).

Some effects produced by the influence of a centripetal force upon a space traveler in free fall:

1. Suppose that a passenger in a space ship is coasting through space at a high velocity with the rocket engines off. He is in free fall. Suddenly the engines are turned on, and the ship executes a sharp right-angle turn. He is thrown by his own impetus against the wall of the ship, and its thrust is felt throughout his body. The wall forces him into the new direction taken by the ship.

2. Now suppose the passenger is again coasting in free fall when suddenly a super-high-density body flashes by and swings the ship into the same sharp right-angle turn by gravitational attraction. *He feels nothing;* in fact, he remains in free fall. It is not the wall of the ship but the new gravitational field that changes his direction. The field acts equally on all particles of both the ship and his body, so that there is no thrust between any of them.

3. Now suppose that the passenger (in free fall) is floating horizontally in the center of the cabin and a companion is spinning him rapidly about

a vertical axis. He feels a force of several g's; for example, in his neck, because it is the tension in his neck that keeps his head attached to his body, just as in example 1, it is the wall of the ship that forces him to change his direction.

Note that the magnitude of the field is immaterial. A man in a vehicle falling onto a superdense star at an acceleration of 1000 g's would feel as weightless as if he were at rest in distant space. But if something held him up, he would be crushed.

Some typical errors about free fall:

1. Jules Verne in "From The Earth to The Moon" fired his passengers out of a gun. At a point where the opposite gravitational fields of the earth and moon just cancelled, they experienced weightlessness for the first time. They would have experienced it throughout the voyage after leaving the muzzle of the gun and the earth's atmosphere.

2. Another author dropped his passengers in a (presumably) sealed tube through the center of the earth to the other side. Inside the earth, the gravitational field varies linearly from zero at the center to 1 g at the ends. They experienced weightlessness only at the center. They would have experienced it all the time (provided the tube contained no air).

Some effects of free fall:

1. If a passenger jumps off the floor, he will rise until his head hits the ceiling, no matter if it is 100 feet up.

2. Water cannot be poured from a bottle. If it is squeezed out of a rubber bottle, it will assume a spherical state and remain in midair, floating in a straight line (relative to the vehicle).

3. The passenger will feel as if he were falling.

4. The passenger will lose all sense of balance and direction, due to the non-action of the otolith organs in the inner ear.

As nobody has been in free fall for more than a minute, it is not yet known whether people can adapt themselves to effects 3 and 4. The next year may bring an answer to this question, when passengers may be put into free-fall paths for many minutes.

Free fall is also defined as "zero-g."

fuel. *See* PROPELLANT.

fuel, atomic. *See* ATOMIC FUEL.

fuel, exotic. *See* EXOTIC FUEL.

fusion, nuclear. The release of ATOMIC ENERGY due to the combination of two or more atoms forming an atom of a different element. Some of the matter in the original atoms is converted into energy. *See also* PLASMA PINCH.

FZG-76. Alternative German designation for V-1.

G

g. Symbol for ACCELERATION DUE TO GRAVITY.

G. Symbol for the GRAVITATIONAL CONSTANT.

GAM. Guided aircraft missile.

GAM-63. Air Force designation for RASCAL.

GAM-72. Air Force designation for QUAIL.

gantry. Short name for GANTRY TOWER.

gantry tower. A structure adjacent to a vertically launched missile that permits service and inspection of all parts of the missile prior to launching. The gantry tower also supports the missile against wind gusts before launching. It is rolled away from the missile before launching. Gantry crane. Gantry scaffold.

GAPA. Ground-to-air pilotless aircraft.

GAR. Guided aircraft rocket.

GAR-1A. Air Force designation for FALCON I.

GAR-2A. Air Force designation for FALCON II.

Genie. Air Force air-to-air rocket missile. Nuclear warhead. Originally unguided, but a guided version is under development. Solid propellant. Range: 1.5 miles. (Also designated MB-1.)

geodesy. The branch of applied mathematics and surveying science concerned with measurement of terrestrial gravitational forces and the size and shape of bodies in space by analysis of gravitational forces associated with those bodies.

GM. Guided missile.

Goddard, Dr. Robert H. October 5, 1882—August 10, 1945. Considered to be the "father of modern rocketry." Designed and flew first liquid-fuel (liquid oxygen-gasoline) rocket on March 5, 1926 in Auburn, Mass. Dr. Goddard developed many rocket principles, including the following:
  Basic bazooka (1918)
  Liquid-fuel rocket motor (1926)
  First hypersonic rocket
  Gyroscopic steering apparatus for rockets
  Vane steering for rockets
  Patented step-rocket principle.

Golem. Class of USSR underwater missiles.

—*Golem I.* Underwater-to-surface missile. Towed by submarines. At launch site, a chamber at tail of missile is filled with water to ensure vertical positioning. This chamber breaks away shortly after missile leaves the water. Peak ceiling: 142 miles.

—*Golem II.* Underwater missile. Similar to the T-2 IRBM but uses nitric acid-alcohol propellant, in order to increase storage capacity. Peak ceiling: 244 miles.

—*Golem III.* Submarine-to-air or ground-to-air missile. Solid propellant. Launching depth: approximately 650 feet.

Goose. Air Force surface-to-air and surface-to-surface guided missile. Inertial guidance. A turbojet with over 5000 pounds thrust. Zero-launched by a solid-propellant, jato-type booster with 100,000 pounds of thrust at take-off. Range: over 2000 miles. Speed: in the high subsonic range. (Also designated SM-73.)

grain. The extruded length into which solid propellants are formed.

—*multi-perforated single cylindrical grain.* A rocket solid propellant with several perforations parallel to the longitudinal axis. All the burning surfaces are approximately the same distance apart.

—*multiple grain.* An assembly of solid-propellant tubular grains inside a rocket motor such that only exterior surfaces of the grains are combustible. Total combustion surface, and therefore thrust, decreases as burning proceeds.

—*star grain.* A rocket solid propellant with an internal, star-shaped cross-section.

gravitational constant. A constant quantity equal to the product of the gravitational force between two particles and the square of the distance between them divided by the product of their masses. It is commonly written "G", and has a value equal to 6.67×10^{-8} in the centimeter-gram-second system.

The force between two particles of known mass at a known distance apart may be computed as shown below.

The equation for G may be written

$$G = \frac{Fd^2}{m_1 m_2},\qquad(1)$$

where

m_1 = mass of first particle in grams,
m_2 = mass of second particle in grams,

d = distance between them in cms,
F = force between them in dynes, and
G = gravitational constant = 6.67×10^{-8}.

Transposing equation 1:

$$F = \frac{Gm_1m_2}{d^2}, \tag{2}$$

which is the more usual form of equation 1.

A homogeneous spherical body may be treated as a particle of equal mass located at its center (as far as its exterior gravitational effects are concerned).

Example: To calculate the force between two homogeneous spheres, each weighing 1 kilogram, and separated by 10 cms between centers:

$$F = \frac{Gm_1m_2}{d^2} \tag{3}$$

$$= \frac{6.67 \times 10^{-8} \times 1000 \times 1000}{100}$$

$$= 6.67 \times 10^{-4}$$

$$= .000667 \text{ dyne.}$$

Similarly, the acceleration due to gravity on a planet of known mass and radius can be computed. Equation 2 now becomes:

$$mf = F = \frac{GMm}{r^2}, \tag{4}$$

where

f = acceleration due to gravity
M = mass of planet
m = mass of a body on the planet's surface
r = radius of planet.

That is:

$$f = \frac{GM}{r^2}. \tag{5}$$

gravity, acceleration due to.   *See* ACCELERATION DUE TO GRAVITY.

Green Quail.   Air Force surface-to-surface decoy missile.

ground support equipment.   All ground (non-flyable) equipment that is used to test and service a missile prior to launching. In some cases, it includes equipment associated with a missile, including guidance equipment.

GSE.   Ground support equipment.

guidance, missile.   Direction and regulation of a missile to a target or a point in space. Guidance equipment may be located in the missile, on the ground, in a "mother" vehicle, or may be any combination thereof. Also, guidance signals may be received from the target by homing missiles.

—beam guidance. A means of missile guidance (also termed beam-rider guidance) used against a moving target. The target is, in general, an aircraft or another missile. A ground radar tracks the target with a beam whose central axis establishes the line connecting the target and the radar. The missile flies along the beam until it hits the target. The beam is polarized in such a way that the missile, once off the central beam axis, can tell which way to steer in order to head back toward the center of the beam. The missile may be gyro-stabilized.

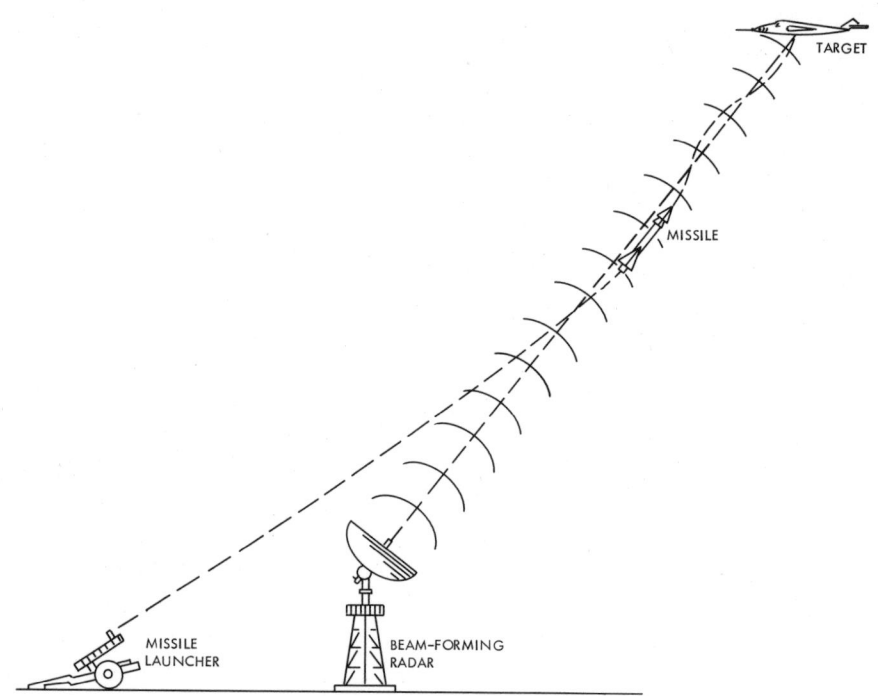

Fig. 10. Beam Guidance   (Von Nostrand's Scientific Encyclopedia, D. Van Nostrand Company, Inc.)

—celestial-navigation guidance. A means of missile guidance to a stationary target, by automation of standard celestial navigation techniques.

—collision-course guidance. A type of missile guidance in which a missile is directed toward a moving target in a path that anticipates the motion of the target and flies not toward but ahead of the target's present position. This path may or may not be a straight line, *i.e.* a "constant-bearing course." Guidance may be beam-rider, command, or homing.

—command guidance.   A means of guidance of missiles or drones in which personnel or a computer in a remote location guides the missile by radio or other signals. In a computer-operated system, ground radars obtain range, elevation, and azimuth data on both missile and target. A ground computer calculates corrections to the missile's path as required to secure a hit. These corrections are transmitted via a radio link to the missile, where they are received and interpreted by the missile's computer and reference system as autopilot signals. Guidance to a moving target may be pursuit-course, collision-course, or proportional navigation. When the control station is mobile, it is sometimes called the "mother" ship or plane. Figure 11 shows the principle of operation of a generalized optical command system.

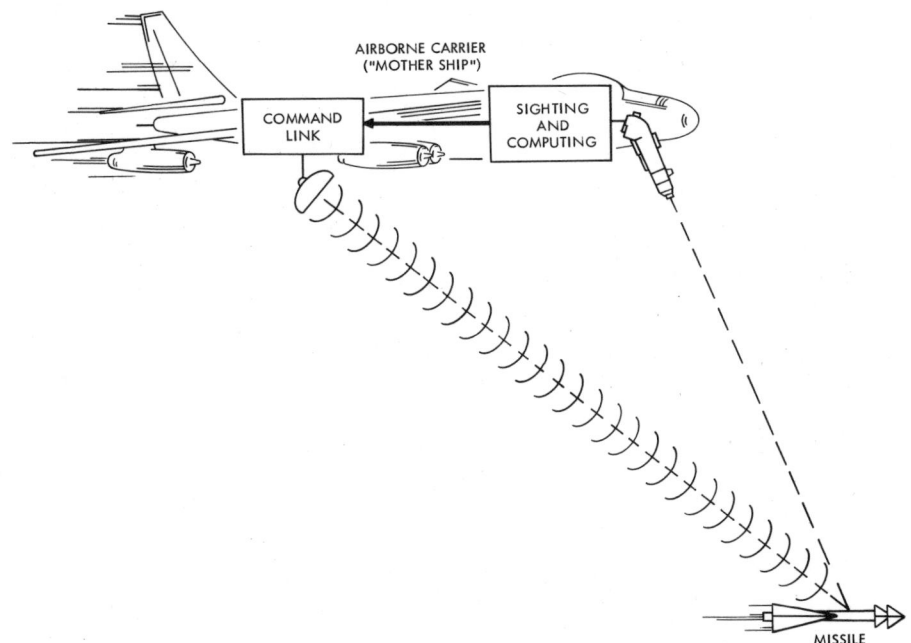

FIG. 11.   Generalized Optical Command System   (Van Nostrand's Scientific Encyclopedia, D. Van Nostrand Company. Inc.)

—constant-bearing course guidance.   The form of collision-course guidance in which the missile flies toward the target in a path that approximates a straight line for short distances. (*See* figure 12.) Strictly speaking, the path is a great circle.

—Doppler guidance.   A means of missile guidance using the DOPPLER EFFECT. CW signals from a ground station are fed continuously to a missile,

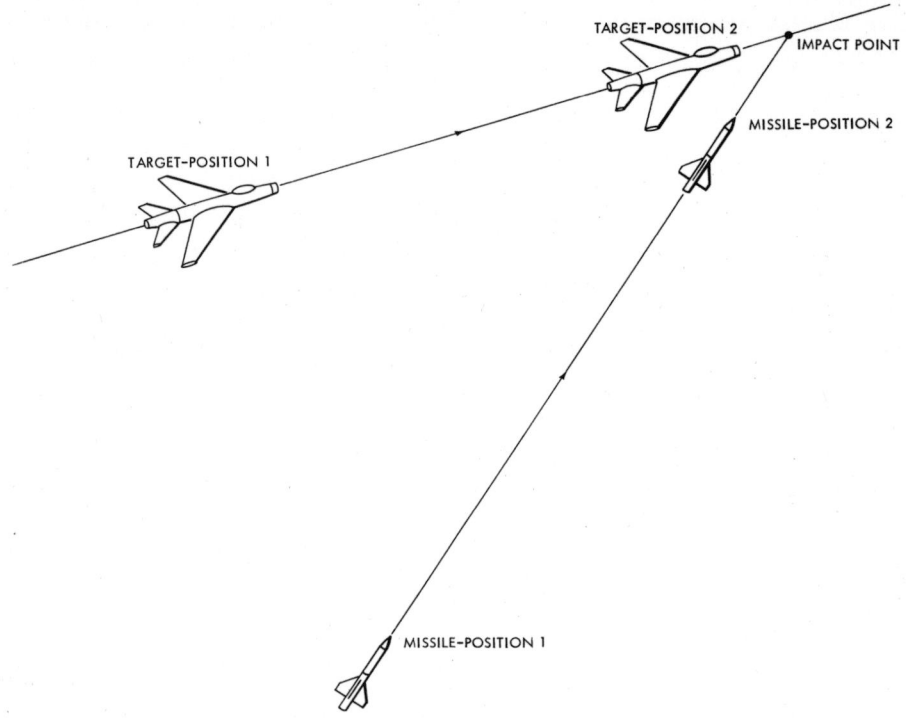

FIG. 12.   Constant-Bearing Course

where the frequency is doubled and the signals reradiated. The relative velocity between the missile and the ground station causes a frequency change: $f_2 = f_1 \left(1 - \dfrac{v}{c} \right)$ approximately, where

f_1 = frequency radiated by the missile,
f_2 = frequency received by the ground station,
v = velocity component of missile away from ground station, and
c = velocity of light.

Shift $= \Delta f = f_1 - f_2$

$$= f_1 - f_1 \left(1 - \frac{v}{c} \right)$$

$$= \frac{v}{c} f_1$$

The return signals at the ground station are mixed with a control signal. Frequency f_2 and, thereby, v are derived from the beat frequency between the return and control signals. With several ground stations, it is possible to calculate the acceleration and position of the missile at any instant. An accuracy of about 6 inches at 100-mile ranges is obtainable.

—Doppler radar guidance. A means of missile guidance using radar in conjunction with the DOPPLER EFFECT. A missile is provided with two antennas which transmit cw signals to the ground; from the frequency shifts of the echo signals and the orientation of the antennas, ground velocity

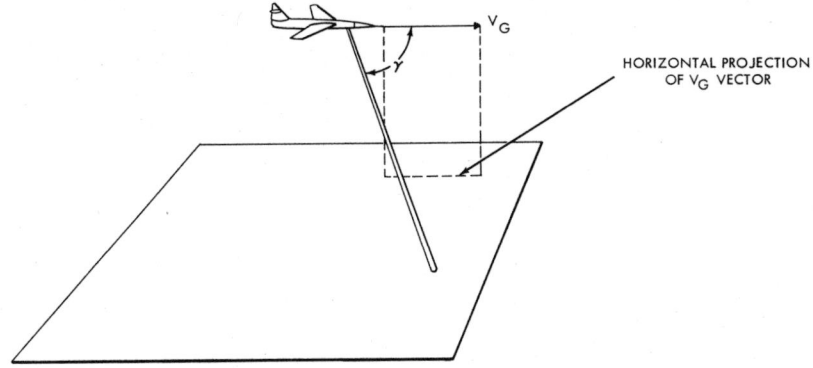

FIG. 13. Doppler Radar Guidance: Missile and Beam

and drift angle are computed. Figure 13 shows a missile traveling horizontally and transmitting a radar beam to the ground.

If

V_G = ground speed,
c = velocity of light,
f = transmitted frequency,
Δf = frequency shift (increase), and
γ = angle between transmitted beam and ground speed,

then

$$\Delta f = \frac{2V_G}{c} f \cos \gamma. \tag{1}$$

(This equation contains a factor of 2 not in the equation under Doppler guidance because here the radar beam is *reflected* from the ground.)

Therefore:

$$V_G = \frac{c\Delta f}{2f \cos \gamma}. \tag{2}$$

Points of beam intersection with the ground having equal values of γ, *i.e.* equal frequency shifts, lie on a hyperbola. Figure 14, a ground plan looking vertically down, shows six such hyperbolas, corresponding to dif-

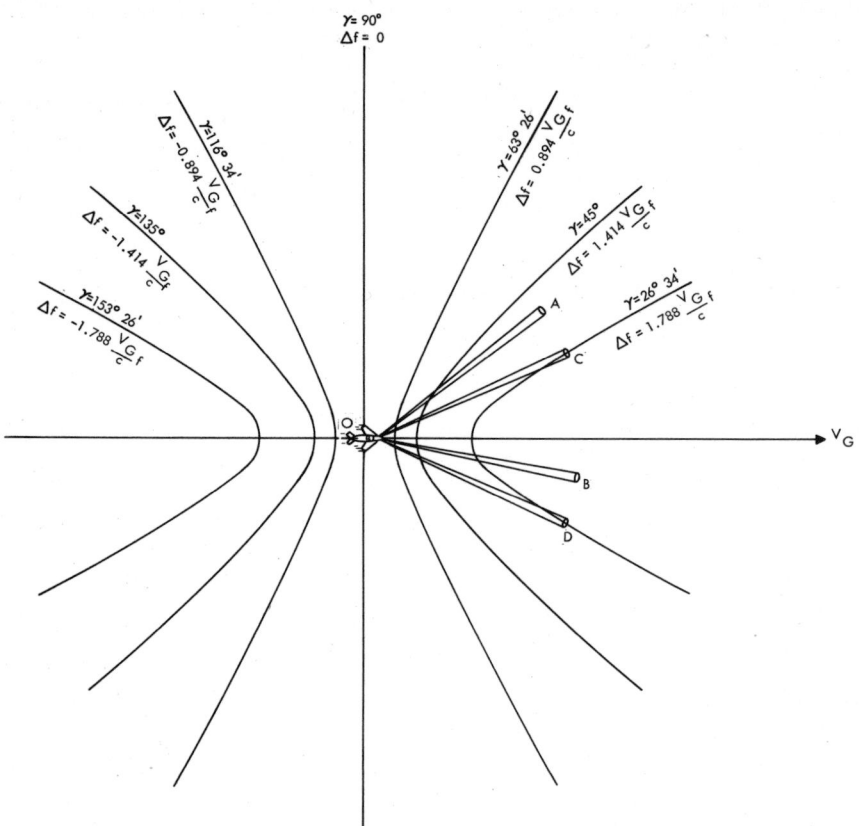

FIG. 14. Doppler Radar Guidance: Effect of Frequency Shifts on Beam Positions

ferent values of γ and Δf. Actually the "vertical" (on paper) axis through the missile is the limiting case of a seventh hyperbola, corresponding to $\gamma = 90°$, $\Delta f = 0$.

Beams OA and OB are the beams transmitted (at equal inclinations to the vertical) to the ground by the two respective antennas. As the beams are not centered about V_G, they are at different values of γ and cause different frequency shifts. Frequency shift for beam OA is between $1.414 \dfrac{\overline{V_G}}{c} f$ and $1.788 \dfrac{\overline{V_G}}{c} f$. The shift of beam OB is greater than $1.788 \dfrac{V_G}{c} f$.

A servomechanism rotates the two antennas until the frequency shifts in the return signals are equal. The antennas are now centered about V_G, and the beams are OC and OD, for both of which the frequency return happens to be $1.788 \dfrac{V_G}{c} f$.

When the frequency shifts are equal, the line bisecting the angle between the antenna axes gives the direction of V_G, whose value is computed from equation 2.

If the direction of V_G does not coincide with the longitudinal axis of the missile, there is evidence of drift. The angle between V_G and the missile axis is the drift angle.

The above discussion, for simplicity, has considered horizontal velocities only. The technique can be elaborated so as to compute ground speed when the missile has a vertical component of velocity.

—homing guidance.   *See* HOMING.

—inertial guidance.   A means of guiding a missile or aircraft to a stationary target of known location. By knowing the initial or check point position and sensing all movements, present position can be continuously computed. Thus, by sensing deviations from a required position at any time, a signal can be developed to bring the missile to the desired point in space.

The basic principle can be explained by describing the form used in current ICBM's prior to BURNOUT. Three ACCELEROMETERS are mounted on a platform held angularly rigid in space by gyro-operated servos. Each accelerometer measures acceleration along one of three orthogonal coordinate axes. The accelerometer outputs are integrated twice, giving missile present position.

For the sake of simplicity, assume that one of the accelerometers is oriented vertically. This one senses not only the actual vertical upward component of acceleration, but gravity, and therefore gives too high a reading. A correction for gravity is obtained by computing the instantaneous value of gravity from the computed present position.

The correction is fed back to the vertical accelerometer, or all three accelerometers in the more general case where none of them are oriented vertically. The corrected information on position is then fed to controls in the rocket propulsion system.

—infrared guidance.   A means of missile guidance in which the missile tracks and pursues a moving target by detecting infrared radiation from the target's motor. Used in PASSIVE HOMING.

—loran guidance.   A means of guiding a missile or aircraft to a stationary target of known location, employing loran, *i.e.* hyperbolic navigation. The principle of loran (long-range navigation) is that the position of a missile or aircraft can be determined by comparing its distance from three fixed stations (master and two slaves). It is necessary to know, not the distances themselves, but merely by how much these distances differ from one another. In this way, a "fix" can be made by locating the missile at the intersection of two hyperbolas. This is because a hyperbola is the locus of points whose

distances from two fixed points have a constant difference. As the distances themselves need not be known, it is not necessary for the missile to carry a radar transmitter, which would be impracticable for long ranges.

In loran guidance, this principle is used, not to ascertain the location of the missile, but to guide the missile to a fixed target. The missile is guided along one of two hyperbolas to its intersection with the other, as described below. The target is at the intersection.

Figure 15 shows the target, three stations, missile, and the two hyper-

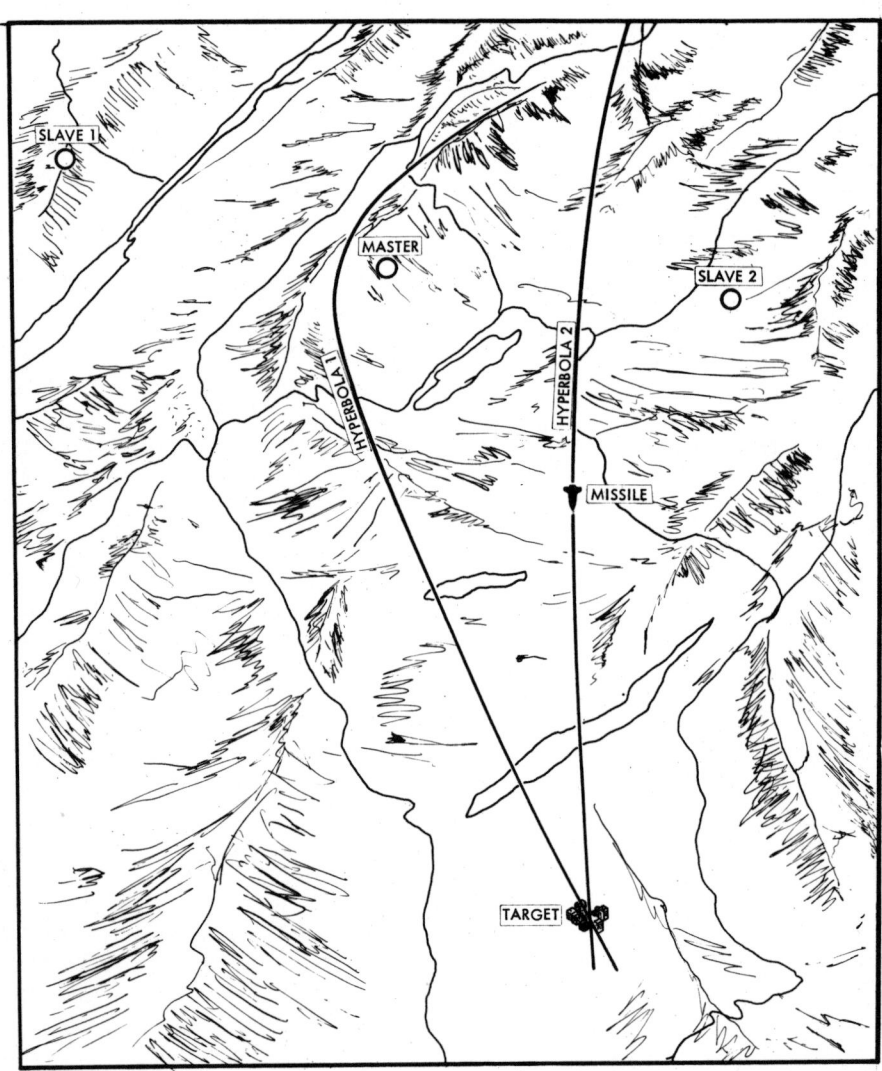

Fɪɢ. 15. Loran Guidance

bolas superimposed upon a map. The distances of the target from the master and two slaves, respectively, are measured on the map. From these it is computed that:

1. The target is 50 miles farther from slave 1 than it is from the master.
2. The target is 10 miles farther from the master than it is from slave 2.

From conclusion 1 we know that the target lies on hyperbola 1, which is the locus of points the difference of whose distance from the master and slave 1 equals 50 miles. From conclusion 2 we know that the target lies on hyperbola 2, which is the locus of points the difference of whose distances from the master and slave 2 equals 10 miles. It is decided to guide the missile along hyperbola 2, as being the straighter of the two curves and so requiring less consumption of fuel.

The missile receives a set of signals (pips) from all three stations. The signals are sent out simultaneously. (The master controls the slaves, which are equidistant from it. The time for the master's control signals to reach the slaves is compensated for by a delay line for the master's own outgoing signals.)

The missile "sees" two displays. One is the pip from the master in conjunction with the pip from slave 1. Normally, these pips coincide when the missile is equidistant from the master and slave 1. When the missile is 50 miles farther from slave 1 than from the master, *i.e.* is on hyperbola 1, the pips are a certain distance apart. An adjustment is made so that the pips will coincide for this inequality of distance, not for equidistance. The other display is the pip from the master and the pip from slave 2. These pips are likewise adjusted so that when the missile is 10 miles farther from the master than from slave 2, *i.e.* is on hyperbola 2, the pips coincide.

The missile automatically travels along such a path as to keep the master and slave 2 pips in coincidence, *i.e.* along hyperbola 2. Meanwhile the master and slave 1 pips approach one another. When they coincide, the missile "knows" that it is on hyperbola 1 and therefore over the target. It then drops onto the target.

The same principle applies for a drone aircraft carrying a missile; when the pips coincide, the drone drops the missile.

For the sake of simplicity, the problem has been presented in two dimensions, on a "flat earth." For long ranges, the curves are not hyperbolas but the intersections of hyperboloids with a sphere.

—phases of guidance. The three phases through which a guided missile may (but need not necessarily) pass on its course to the target: 1) launch, by jet motor, rocket, or catapult; 2) guidance, by beam or radio command from the ground; 3) homing onto the target. (*See also under* MISSILE.)

—proportional-navigational guidance. A type of missile guidance in which the missile flies toward a moving target in a path such that the turning rate

of the missile is proportional to the angular velocity of the line of sight (usually measured by rate gyros). Such a path is intermediate between the pursuit course and constant-bearing course, being curved but requiring less turning rates than those of a pursuit course. Guidance may be beam-rider, command, or homing.

—pursuit-course guidance.   A type of missile guidance in which the missile flies toward a moving target in a path such that a tangent to it at the point occupied by the missile at any instant passes through the target. (*See* figure 16.) In other words, the missile is always moving in the direction of the

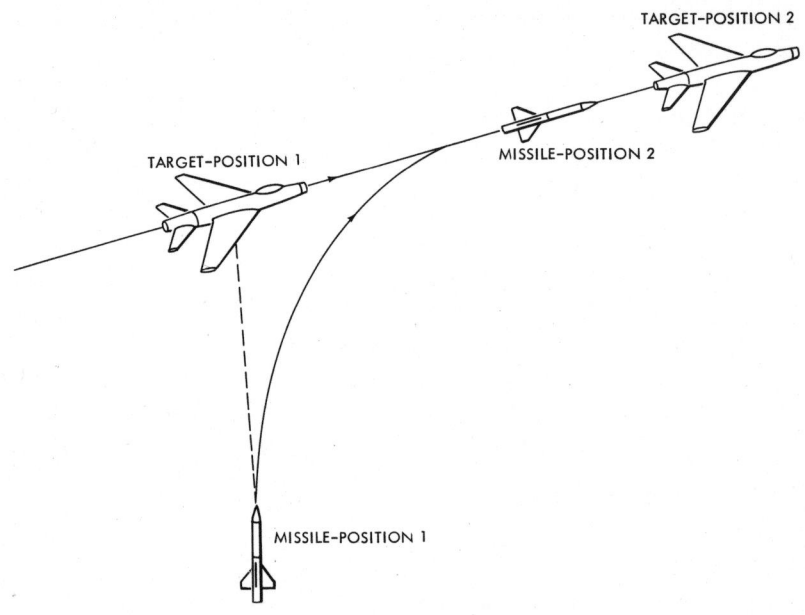

FIG. 16.   Pursuit Course

target. This path is consequently curved. The missile eventually collides with the target owing to its greater velocity. This is the simplest course for a missile to pursue but requires large turning rates toward the end, thereby impeding maneuverability. Guidance may be beam-rider, command, or homing.

guided missile.   *See under* MISSILE.

H

hardware.   Military term for usable equipment. *Colloq.*

Harvest Moon.   Proposed manned satellite. First stage is based on the

Navaho booster design, consisting of several rocket engines of many thousands of pounds thrust.

Hawk I.   Army and Marine Corps surface-to-air missile. Used primarily against low-flying craft, with radar instrumentation. Solid propellant. Is carried on launcher from which three missiles can be fired in rapid succession. Is fired through balloon-like domes protecting launchers against weather.

head compartment.   *See* Nose cone.

heat barrier.   *See* Thermal barrier.

heat shield.   A protective covering often incorporating a heat sink that prevents heat damage to critical parts. Certain nose cones rely on heat shields to protect internal mechanisms from the thermal effects of Re-entry. (*See* figure 17.)

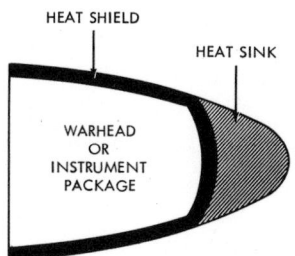

Fig. 17.   Heat Shield and Heat Sink

heat sink.   A mass of heat-conductive material so placed as to conduct heat away from sensitive areas and concentrate it in an area where it cannot cause damage. (*See* figure 17.)

Heaviside layer.   E-layer of the ionosphere.

HEF.   High-energy fuel.

Hidyne.   Common name for hydrazone.

Hohmann orbit.   *See* Tangential ellipse.

hold.   Unscheduled delay in count-down or launching sequence. *Colloq.*

homing.   Automatic guidance of a missile to a moving target by either a return echo radar signal or radiation from the target. Guidance may be collision-course, proportional-navigation, or pursuit-course.

—*active homing.*   Automatic guidance of a missile to a moving target. The missile carries its own target illuminating and detection system, such as radar, and closes in on the target by means of the received target data. (*See* figure 18.)

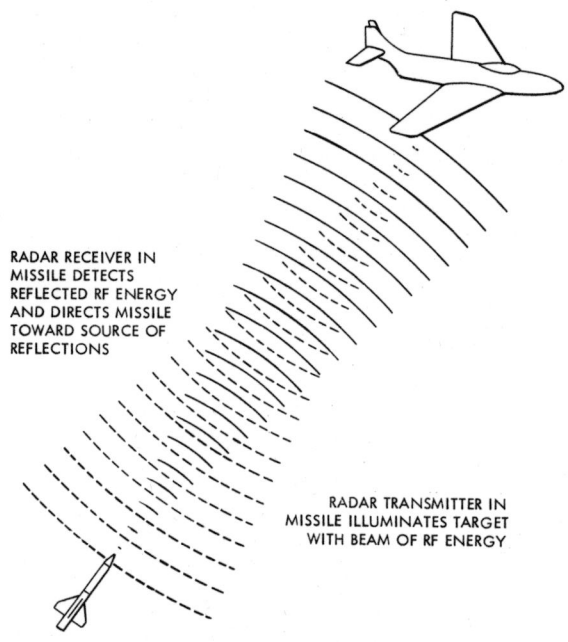

RADAR RECEIVER IN
MISSILE DETECTS
REFLECTED RF ENERGY
AND DIRECTS MISSILE
TOWARD SOURCE OF
REFLECTIONS

RADAR TRANSMITTER IN
MISSILE ILLUMINATES TARGET
WITH BEAM OF RF ENERGY

FIG. 18.   Air-to-Air Active Homing

—*passive homing.*   Automatic guidance of a missile to a moving target by radiation from the target. This radiation may be radio waves, or infrared rays from the target's motor. (*See* figure 19.)

—*semi-active homing.*   Automatic guidance of a missile to a moving target by a return echo radar signal. The original radar signal is transmitted from the ground, not from the missile. (*See* figure 20.)

Honest John.   Army surface-to-surface artillery type rocket. Used to provide close fire support for ground operations. Solid propellant. A slow spin is provided by spin rockets. Is fired from a mobile, self-propelled launcher, and can carry a nuclear warhead.

Hopi.   Navy air-to-surface medium-range missile. Designed for carrier aircraft. Capable of carrying a 650-pound hydrogen warhead.

Hound Dog.   Air Force air-to-surface ramjet-powered missile. Successor to RASCAL. One carried under each wing of a B-52 aircraft, which carries a computer to permit simultaneous shots at two different targets. Guidance probably inertial navigation corrected by Doppler radar.

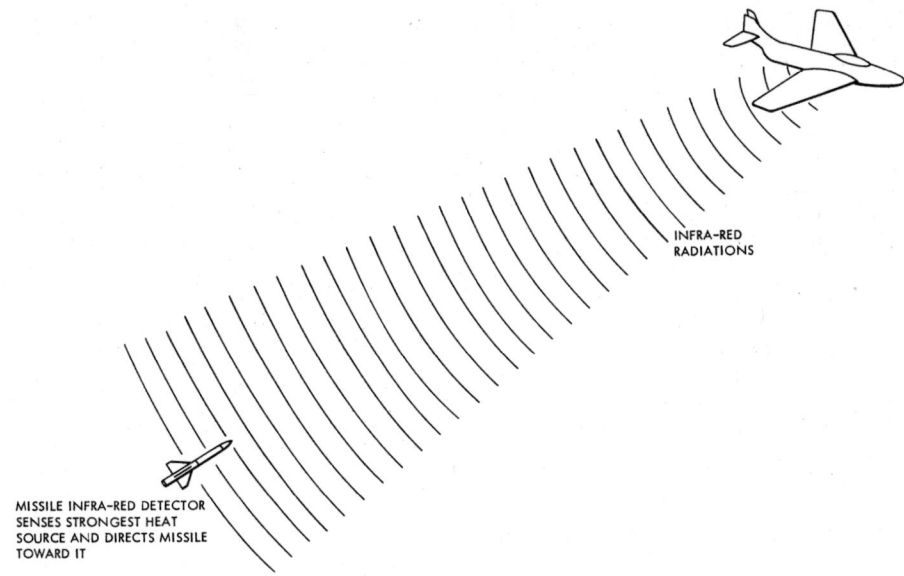

INFRA-RED
RADIATIONS

MISSILE INFRA-RED DETECTOR
SENSES STRONGEST HEAT
SOURCE AND DIRECTS MISSILE
TOWARD IT

Fig. 19.   Passive Homing

human engineering.   The tailoring of aircraft and spacecraft to meet the physiological and psychological requirements of the crew.

hybrid rocket.   *See under* ROCKET.

hydrazine.   A liquid base, $NH_2 \cdot NH_2$, or one of the organic bases derived from it such as phenylhydrazine. Used as a liquid PROPELLANT.

hydrazone.   EXOTIC FUEL formed by the action of hydrazine or one of its derivatives on a compound containing the carbonyl group, CO. Used in first stage of JUPITER-C.

hydroduct.   An underwater RAMJET. It uses ambient seawater as an "atmosphere" and a water-reagent for fuel. The seawater is raised to ram pressure by an inlet diffuser and ejected from the rear nozzle as steam.

hydroponics.   A branch of agricultural science concerned with growing plants in a controlled chemical environment, as opposed to natural growth in soil. This is accomplished by growing food plants in water containing chemical nutrients and using lamps to simulate sunlight. In a closed system, such as a space vehicle on a long flight, there is the added advantage that carbon dioxide is absorbed and oxygen is released.

hydropulse.   An underwater PULSE JET.

hydroturbojet.   An underwater TURBOJET.

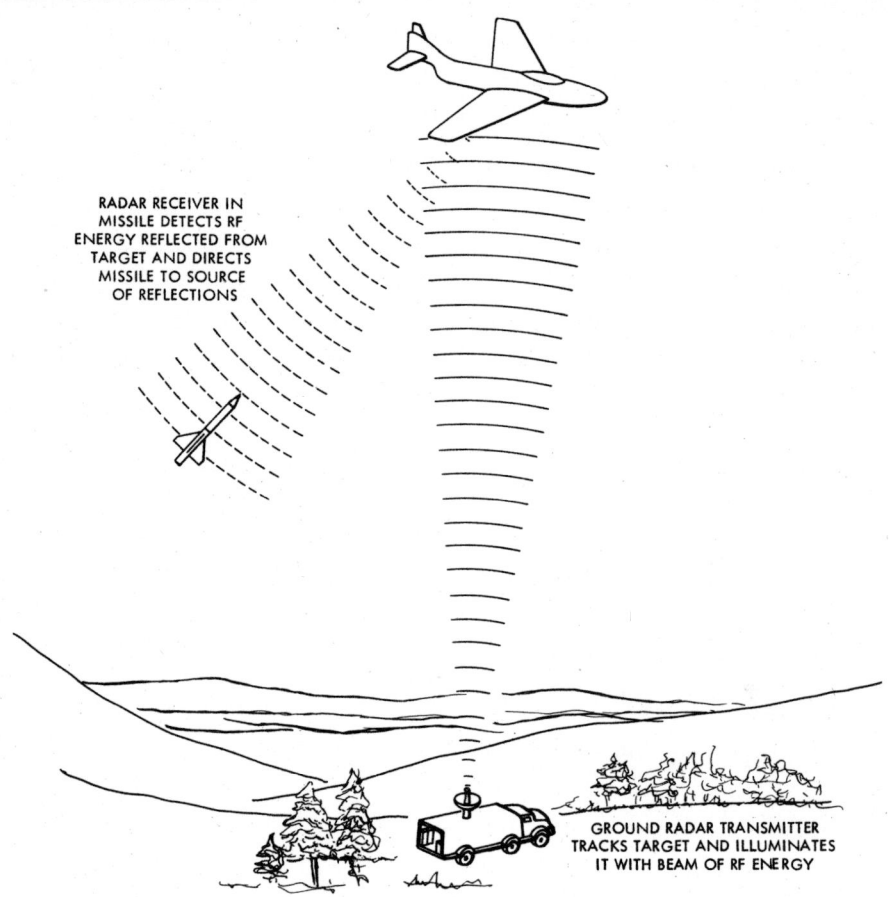

RADAR RECEIVER IN MISSILE DETECTS RF ENERGY REFLECTED FROM TARGET AND DIRECTS MISSILE TO SOURCE OF REFLECTIONS

GROUND RADAR TRANSMITTER TRACKS TARGET AND ILLUMINATES IT WITH BEAM OF RF ENERGY

FIG. 20. Semi-Active Homing

Hydyne. Variant of Hidyne. Common name for HYDRAZONE.

hyperbolic guidance. LORAN GUIDANCE.

hyperbolic propellant. *See under* PROPELLANT.

hyperoxia. *See* HYPOXIA.

hypersonic. Faster than Mach 5. (*See* MACH.)

hyperthermia. *See* HYPOTHERMIA.

hypochloremia. Sickness due to atmospheric humidity.

hypothermia. Sickness due to atmospheric temperature.

hypoxia. Sickness due to lack of oxygen.

I

ICBM. Intercontinental ballistic missile.

IGOR. **1.** Intercept ground optical recorder. A telescopic camera used in missile range tests. Range coverage: up to 100,000 feet. Focal length: 108 inches.
2. Alternate designation for USSR ME missile.

IGY satellite. One or other of the artificial satellites developed for purposes of the International Geophysical Year. (*See under* Satellite, artificial.)

IM. Interceptor missile.

IM-70. Navy designation for Talos.

immersion suit. *See* Pressure suit.

impulse, specific. Measure of a rocket's merit:

$$\frac{\text{thrust}}{\text{lb liberated/sec}} = \frac{1}{g} \times \text{exhaust velocity.}$$

(*See also* Rocket.)

impulse, total. The product of the average thrust of a jet in pounds times the burning time in seconds.

IMU. Inertial measurement unit.

inactive homing. Passive homing.

inertial guidance. *See under* Guidance, missile.

infrared guidance. *See under* Guidance, missile.

inherent stability. *See* Stability, inherent.

instability, dynamic. *See* Sonance.

instrumentation package. The portion of a missile or artificial satellite containing telemetry equipment and its power source. *See also* Recovery package.

intercontinental ballistic missile. Ballistic missile having a range of 6500 miles (approximate). Examples: Atlas and Titan.

intermediate range ballistic missile. Ballistic missile having a range between 200 and 1500 miles (approximate). Examples: Jupiter and Thor.

IOC. Initial operational capability.

ion engine. Engine of an ION ROCKET in which thrust is achieved by expelling ions at high exhaust velocities.

ionosphere. An ionized layer of the atmosphere much used as a reflector of lower-frequency radio signals. (It is penetrated by higher-frequency radio waves.) The ionosphere consists of at least four layers, D, E, F1, and F2, at heights varying from 30-50 to 175-250 miles. The ionosphere thus overlaps the mesosphere and thermosphere. The ionization is believed to be produced principally by sunlight. The region generally rises to a greater altitude at night. The E layer was formerly called the "Kennelly-Heaviside layer."

ion rocket. *See under* ROCKET.

IRBM. INTERMEDIATE-RANGE BALLISTIC MISSILE.

Iris. A solid-propellant research missile. Designed to lift a 100-pound instrument ion package to an altitude of approximately 200 miles.

isostatic. Under equal pressure from all sides.

I_{sp}. Symbol for specific impulse. *See* IMPULSE, SPECIFIC.

J

J-1. USSR surface-to-surface guided missile. Similar to German V-1. Medium-range, low-level. Launched from runway or sled. Carries equipment to cut out detection radar. Peak ceiling: approximately 4 miles.

J-2. USSR anti-submarine air-breathing missile. Similar to SNARK. Can also carry 3200 pounds of supplies to troops. Peak ceiling: 6.8 miles.

J-3. USSR surface-to-sea ramp-launched missile. Supersonic version of J-2 with same fuselage and instrumentation but with swept-back wings, a ramjet, and two booster rockets. Peak ceiling: 10.25 miles.

jamming. The blocking of a radio or television channel.

—*active jamming.* The radiation or re-radiation of electromagnetic energy with the object of impairing the use of specific channels.

—*barrage jamming.* The simultaneous jamming of a number of adjacent channels.

—*passive jamming.* The use of a CONFUSION REFLECTOR against radar.

—*spot jamming.* The jamming of a specific channel.

jato unit. Jet-assisted take-off unit. A rocket booster engine used to provide thrust for aircraft and missiles at take-off. The jato unit is generally expendable.

—*jato cant point.* The intersection of jato chamber axis and nozzle center-lines.

jet. A type of aircraft or missile engine which derives its velocity from the intake of air at the forward end, combustion of fuel, and ejection of combustion products at high velocity at the rear end. Ramjets have no moving parts (excepting a valve used in the pulse-jet types). Turbojets, turbo-props, etc., have rotating parts. (*See also* specific types of jets.)

jetavator. Exhaust gas vanes used to control or steer rockets during powered flight.

JPL. Jet Propulsion Laboratory.

Juno II. A combination of sixteen Army rockets, in four stages, used to launch the lunar probe and artificial planet PIONEER IV on March 3, 1959. The assembly comprises a "tub" of fifteen scaled-down Sergeants mounted on top of a Jupiter. The first stage consists of the Jupiter. The second stage is an outer circle of eleven Sergeants, in the tub. The third stage is an inner circle of three Sergeants. The fourth stage is one, central, Sergeant which carries the payload. During count-down, the tub begins to spin, reaching 700 or more rpm; this is done to stabilize the rocket's flight. The rocket accelerates to almost 25,000 mph in four minutes. Length: 76 feet. Weight: 60 tons.

Jupiter. 1. Fifth planet of the solar system.
2. Army surface-to-surface IRBM. Carries a nuclear warhead. Length: 58 feet. Diameter: 9 feet. Range: over 1500 miles.

Jupiter-C. A JUPITER-THOR hybrid. Has been test-flown 3000 miles.

K

Katie. Navy surface-to-surface and anti-submarine rocket missile. Nuclear fission warhead. Launched by shipborne 16-inch guns.

Kelvin scale. Scale on which temperature is measured in "degrees K," one of which equals one Centrigrade degree. Zero on the Kelvin scale is the absolute zero, *viz.:* -273.16 degrees C.

Kennelly-Heaviside layer. E-layer of the IONOSPHERE.

knot. Speed equal to one nautical mile per hour.

Kobra. German-developed, now U. S. Army anti-tank missile. Two stages: the first lifts it off the ground, the second ignites to carry it to the target.

L

Lacrosse. Army surface-to-surface artillery-guided missile. Launched from truck in rear of combat area, guided by forward airborne observer.

landing rocket. *See under* ROCKET.

launch. Sending forth a rocket or missile from a launching pad, rack, ramp, or other device or installation. The missile may be launched under its own power, or by some form of exterior propulsion such as a catapult.—Launching.

—*zero-launch.* Missile launching from a zero-length launcher.

launcher. A mechanism for handling a missile at launching and, in some cases, providing an initial thrust to the missile by hydraulic or other means.

—*retractable launcher.* A launcher that carries a missile or rocket in one position and extends it to a new position for launching.

—*zero-length launcher.* A launcher that merely positions and orientates a missile and provides no thrust or other guidance after firing.

launching dispersion. The departure of a guided missile from the desired flight path during the launching phase.

launch pad. The fixed ground area (platform) from which a missile (generally a rocket) is launched by remote control. The launch site may consist of several launch pads.—Launching pad.

launch point. The point at which a rocket or missile is launched.

launch vehicle. A guided rocket used to place a satellite in orbit or launch a space probe.

light, velocity of. 186,271 miles per second = 2.9977×10^{10} cms per second.

light year. The distance light travels in one year (nearly 6000 trillion miles). An astronomical unit of distance.

liquid fuel. 1. That portion of a liquid propellant exclusive of the oxidizer. 2. Loosely used for "liquid propellant."

liquid propellant. *See* PROPELLANT.

liquid rocket. 1. Rocket using liquid propellant. 2. Short for "liquid propellant."

Little John. Army surface-to-surface artillery-type rocket. Designed to supplement HONEST JOHN. Range: equivalent to medium-to-long-range artillery.

Lobber. Ballistic cargo missile. Designed to deliver rations, ammunition, medicine, communications equipment, and other supplies to front-line troops. The missile and its launcher can be hand-carried by three men.

loran. Long-range navigation.

—loran guidance. *See under* GUIDANCE, MISSILE.

Lorentz contraction. *See* TIME DILATATION.

low-energy primary. Biologically dangerous cosmic-ray particle.

lox. Liquid oxygen.

lunar probe. Investigation of the moon by a rocket, which may: 1) score a direct hit on the moon (figure 217, 2) travel partially around the moon and off into space, 3) go into orbit around the moon, or 4) go around the moon

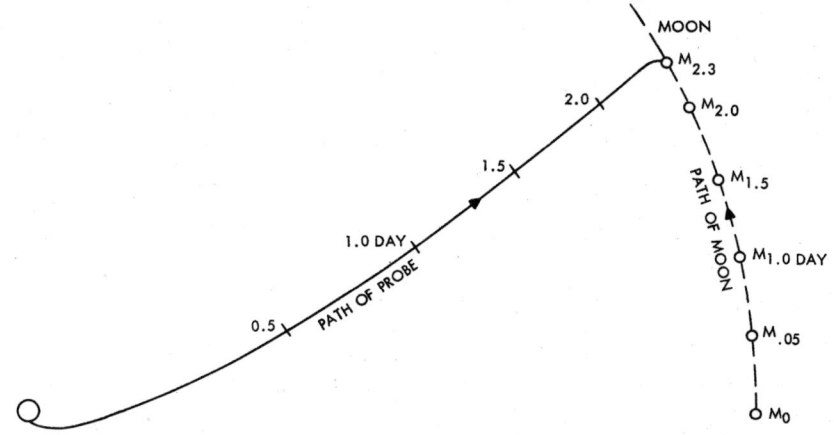

FIG. 21. Lunar Probe Path to Moon, Scoring a Direct Hit (Space Handbook: Astronautics and Its Applications. Staff Report of the Select Committee on Astronautics and Space Exploration (Random House, Inc.))

and return to the earth (figure 22). The rocket carries telemetering instruments to observe lunar phenomena and radio-transmit them to the earth.

Lunik. USSR lunar probe. First earth vehicle to achieve escape velocity. Believed to have gone into orbit around the sun. (*Also see under* SATELLITE, ARTIFICIAL.)

M

M-100A. USSR air-to-air rocket missile. Similar to Falcon. Can be used unguided or with infrared guidance.

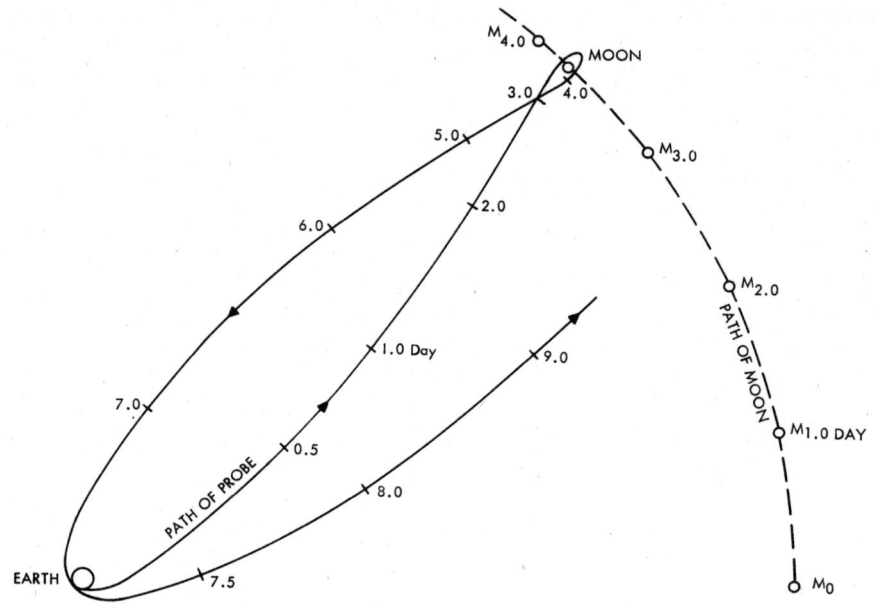

Fɪɢ. 22. Lunar Probe Path Around Moon and Back to Earth   (Space Handbook: Astronautics and Its Applications. Staff Report of the Select Committee on Astronautics and Space Exploration (Random House, Inc.))

M-101.   USSR missile. *See* T-1.

M-102.   USSR missile. *See* T-4.

M-104.   USSR missile. *See* T-3.

M-105.   USSR missile. *See* T-2.

M-2.   USSR surface-to-air and surface-to-surface two-stage guided missile. Launched from mobile units. Developed from Rheintochter, an early German missile.

Mace.   Air Force surface-to-surface guided missile. ATRAN or inertial guidance. Solid propellant. Uses jato 100,000-pound thrust booster, and a 5200-pound thrust turbojet sustainer. Range: 700 miles. Speed: Mach 0.9. (Also designated TM-76.)

Mach.   (After Ernst Mach, 1838-1916, Austrian physicist.) Name applied to various phenomena associated with the relationship between the velocities of sound and a moving body.

—*Mach angle.*   The angle between the path of a body moving with supersonic speed and a Mach line. The sine of the Mach angle equals the ratio of the local speed of sound to the speed of the missile.

—*Mach line.* The path of a theoretical shock wave produced by a microscopic point moving with a velocity above Mach 1.

—*Mach number.* The velocity of a body divided by the velocity of sound at that point. (The velocity of sound decreases with increased altitude.)

—*Mach wave.* An atmospheric shock wave set up in the vicinity of an object moving with a velocity above Mach 1.

magnetic bottle. A magnetic field used to confine a stream of plasma in the "pinch effect," thereby keeping it away from the sides of the container and raising its temperature. (*See* PLASMA PINCH.)

magnetohydrodynamics. The branch of physical science concerned with interaction between a moving fluid capable of conducting electricity, *e.g.* plasma, and a magnetic field.

Marco Polo. Early nickname for VIKING.

Mars. Fourth planet of the solar system.

mass ratio. The ratio of the mass of a rocket at launching to its mass at BURNOUT. Mass ratio for a single-stage rocket is related to VELOCITY RATIO (ratio of velocity at burnout to EXHAUST VELOCITY) by the equation:

$$\text{mass ratio} = e^{(velocity\ ratio)}$$

i.e. velocity ratio = $\log_e$ (mass ratio), where e = 2.71828.

Matador. Air Force surface-to-surface missile. Uses radar/Shanicle system guidance and navigation. Solid propellant. Uses jato 52,000-pound thrust booster and a 4600-pound thrust turbojet sustainer. Range: 700 miles (maximum). Speed: Mach 0.9 (maximum). (Also designated TM-61.)

Matador Mace. *See* MACE.

MB-1. Air Force designation for GENIE.

ME. USSR anti-tank rocket missile. Similar to U.S. BAZOOKA, with same type of launching system but with longer range. (Also designated IGOR.)

meaconing. Measuring and confusing. A means of measuring received electromagnetic signals and instantaneously broadcasting confusion signals at the same frequency. Used to confuse navigation. Example: CONFUSION REFLECTOR.

Mechta. USSR designation for Lunik. *See under* SATELLITE, ARTIFICIAL.

medicine, space. *See* SPACE MEDICINE.

Mercury. 1. First planet of the solar system.
   2. *See* PROJECT MERCURY.

Mercury Astronaut. Title to be given to the pilot selected to man the first PROJECT MERCURY space capsule.

mesosphere. The region between 15 to 20 and 50 miles altitude above the surface of the earth, where photochemical activity is predominant. Coextensive with the chemosphere, according to Chapman; however, according to Wares, the mesosphere lies between 250 and 600 miles altitude.

metagalaxy. The entire appreciable material universe, including all galaxies and all particles, stars, planets, and star clusters in the spaces between galaxies. The regions relatively near to us are called the "inner metagalaxy."

Meteorological satellite. *See under* SATELLITE, ARTIFICIAL.

Microlock network. A network of tracking and monitoring stations used to track missiles and satellites.

micrometeorite. Particles of microscopic size (a few microns to about 100 microns, *i.e.* about 1/250 of an inch), which drop on the earth from outer space. Most of them are too small even to become incandescent in their passage through the atmosphere. Larger micrometeorites may present some hazard to future space ships by causing punctures leading to atmospheric leaks. A large shower of the smaller ones might produce the effect of sandblasting.

minitrack. 1. The track of a miniature transmitter emitting telemeter-type signals.
2. Short for "Minitrack radio."

Minitrack network. A network of U.S. stations placed at different points around the world in order to track the flight of an artificial satellite.

Minitrack radio. A radio receiver that tracks an object equipped with a miniature transmitter emitting telemeter-type signals. Used in tracking artificial satellites, for example.

Minuteman. Air Force ICBM. Will replace ATLAS and TITAN. Solid propellant. Range: 5750 miles. Uses underground launcher. Requires less troops to operate than Atlas or Titan.

MIRAN. Missile ranging. A multi-station, missile ranging system using radar triangulation.

missile. A self-propelled, unmanned vehicle which travels above the earth's surface. It differs from aircraft, which are manned, and projectiles, which are not self-propelled. Missiles are classified in various ways similar to the following examples:
By mission—strategic, tactical.

By deployment—surface-to-air, air-to-air, air-to-surface, etc.

By flight path—ballistic, aerodynamic.

By range—short, medium, intermediate, intercontinental, transcontinental.

By guidance—beam-rider, command, homing, inertial, celestial-navigation, etc.

By function—attack, defense, subterfuge, exploration, and target.

—anti-missile missile.   A guided missile designed to intercept and destroy another missile.

—ballistic missile.   A missile that travels throughout most of its course in a ballistic trajectory, without additional guidance, as a projectile. At the beginning of its course, it is guided so as to set in on the desired trajectory. Guidance is generally performed by rocket engines, computers, gyroscopic devices, etc., controlled from the ground. At BURNOUT, the rocket engines cease to operate, and the front portion of the rocket (nose cone) separates from the rest and travels without guidance to its target in an elliptical path. The greater portion of this path is at such high altitudes as to be, virtually, in a vacuum. Examples of ballistic missiles are the ICBM and IRBM. A pseudo-ballistic type of missile under consideration uses automatically operated rocket motors toward the last portion of its trajectory for course correction and/or reduction in velocity during re-entry.

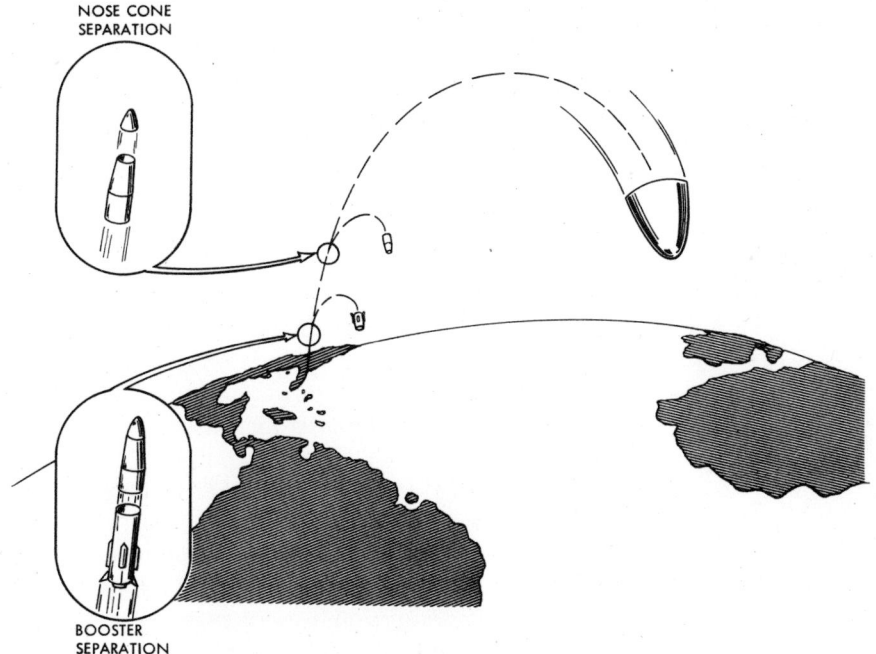

NOSE CONE
SEPARATION

BOOSTER
SEPARATION

FIG. 23.   Flight of an Icbm

—cargo missile.   A ballistic missile used to transport rations, medicine, ammunition, and other supplies to front line troops.

—contra-orbit missile.   Missile sent backward along calculated orbit of an approaching space ship, satellite, or missile, for the purpose of destroying it.

—diversionary missile.   A missile used to draw or distract enemy fire or radar attention from the primary target.

—guided missile.   A missile whose flight path is controlled after launching through part or all of its course. Guided missiles may be classified in three categories:

1. Missiles guided from their launching base (ground, sea, or air) all the way to their target by ground equipment which transmits radio signals to missile-borne equipment. The two principal means of guidance are beamrider and command.

2. Missiles that automatically pursue their target by "homing," *i.e.* by detecting and following signals received from the target. In "active homing," the missile carries its own radar transmitter and tracks the target by the latter's echo signal. In "semi-active homing," the missile carries no transmitter, and the radar signal is transmitted from the ground. In "passive homing," the missile carries no transmitter but tracks the target by radiation from the latter. This radiation may be radio waves or infrared heat rays from the target's motor. Homing is used exclusively on moving targets and over comparatively short ranges.

3. Missiles guided only in the initial phase of their course, the greater part of which is a ballistic, unguided trajectory. They are used only against stationary targets. (*See also* Ballistic missile, *above.*)

Missiles in category 1 may be further classified as surface-to-surface, surface-to-air, air-to-surface, and air-to-air. Missiles in category 2 may be further classified as surface-to-air and air-to-air. Missiles in category 3 are exclusively surface-to-surface. A missile exhibits the behavior of two or even three of these categories during its flight.

Generally speaking, there may be three phases in a guided missile's course. The first is the launching phase, in which the missile is lifted off the ground and given a high velocity, by rocket, catapult, or other device. The second is the ground-guided phase, in which the missile is picked up by a beam or other form of ground control. The third is the homing phase, in which the missile, having approached near to the target, is guided not from the ground but by the target. The three phases are optional. A missile does not necessarily experience all three, but generally does experience at least two of them.

Guidance of missiles to moving targets can also be classified under: Pursuit-course, collision-course, and proportional-navigation.

Five means of guidance primarily suitable for use against stationary targets are: Doppler, Doppler radar, loran, inertial, and celestial-navigation.

—homing missile. A missile guided to a moving target by either a return echo radar signal or radiation from the target. A seeker.

—interceptor missile. Missile launched with the purpose of destroying an enemy flight. Generally, surface-to-air or air-to-air.

—strategic missile. A missile used for bombardment of strategic targets.

—tactical missile. A missile used for direct support of combat operations.

—tandem missile. A configuration for missiles in which stages are stacked together in series and are discarded at burnout of the propellant for each stage. (*See* MULTI-STAGE ROCKET *under* ROCKET.)

missilry. The science of designing, launching, and controlling guided missiles. *See under* MISSILE.

monogole. A monopropellant.

monopropellant. *See under* PROPELLANT.

moon. 1. The earth's only satellite.
  2. Any satellite of a planet. There are 31 satellites in the solar system (not counting the rings of Saturn, which are now known to consist of innumerable small bodies in orbit around the parent planet).

moonwatch. *See* OPERATION MOONWATCH.

MOPTAR. Multi-object phase tracking and ranging system.

Mosquito. Swiss anti-tank missile. Similar to Kobra but more complex.

mother plane, ship. Vehicle containing equipment for controlling another vehicle or vehicles. *Colloq.*

motor, atomic. *See* ATOMIC MOTOR.

motor, rocket. *See* ENGINE, ROCKET.

Mouse. Minimum orbital unmanned satellite, earth. A proposed artificial satellite consisting of a sphere 1 foot in diameter capable of carrying 45 pounds of equipment. To be used in the study of the upper layers of the atmosphere and ultraviolet and X-ray solar radiation. Will describe a polar orbit at a 2000-mile altitude in about 95 minutes.

multi-stage rocket. *See under* ROCKET.

Muskrat. *See* PROJECT MUSKRAT.

N

NACA. National Advisory Committee for Aeronautics. Now succeeded by NASA.

NASA.   National Aeronautics and Space Administration.

nautical mile.   The length of one minute of arc on a sphere of area equal to that of the earth. One nautical mile = 6080.20 feet

$$= \frac{38}{33} \text{ statute miles approximately.}$$

Navaho.   Air Force supersonic, surface-to-surface, winged, guided intercontinental missile. Ramjet propulsion with rocket booster. Inertial and electronic star-tracking guidance. (Also designated SM-64.)

Neptune.   1. Eighth planet of the solar system.
  2. Early designation for VIKING.

Nike.   A class of Army surface-to-air supersonic guided missiles now in operation. The development program provides constant improvement in missile capabilities. Specific models are assigned the names of mythological Greek gods.

—*Nike-Ajax.*   Solid-propellant booster which separates. Fired vertically. Electronically detects evasive action of target and alters course. Undergoing replacement by NIKE-HERCULES.

—*Nike-Hercules.*   Replacing NIKE-AJAX, which it greatly surpasses in destructive power. Ground guidance system uses three radars, a computer, automatic plotting board, etc.

—*Nike-Zeus.*   An improved version of the NIKE-AJAX and NIKE-HERCULES.

nomenclature of artificial satellites.   *See under* SATELLITE, ARTIFICIAL.

NORAD.   NORTH AMERICAN AIR DEFENSE.

North American air defense.   A coordinated defense of North American against attack by missile or aircraft.

nose cone.   Also called RE-ENTRY VEHICLE or head compartment. The front portion of a missile that protects the INSTRUMENTATION PACKAGE, satellite, or WARHEAD during launching and/or RE-ENTRY. In many missiles, the nose cone separates from the remaining portions of the missile at or after BURN-OUT. The nose cone is the only portion of a ballistic missile to fly the ballistic trajectory to the target.

nozzle cant angle.   The angle between nozzle axis and jato centerline at the jato cant point.

nuclear fission.   *See* FISSION, NUCLEAR.

nuclear fusion.   *See* FUSION, NUCLEAR.

nuclear reactor.   *See* REACTOR, NUCLEAR.

O

Oerlikon. Swiss surface-to-air missile. Liquid fuel rocket propulsion and beam-rider guidance.

OpDevFor. OPERATIONAL DEVELOPMENT FORCES.

Operational Development Forces. A Naval force responsible for tactical evaluation of missiles, weapon systems, etc., under fleet operating conditions.

Operation Farside. A series of experiments in which rockets are fired from balloons in the stratosphere. The sixth in the series was fired to an altitude of 4000 miles from a height of 20 miles on October 21, 1957.

Operation Moonwatch. Volunteer visual satellite observing program of the Smithsonian Astrophysical Observatory.

Operation Vanguard. The official U.S.A. artificial satellite development program, assigned to the Navy Department.

orbital bomber. Bombing aircraft capable of speed allowing the craft to circle the earth once or twice in orbit at very high altitude and then glide back to earth.

orbital decay. The gradual reduction in size of a satellite's elliptical orbit, due to air resistance (DRAG). Generally speaking, a satellite is ejected hori-

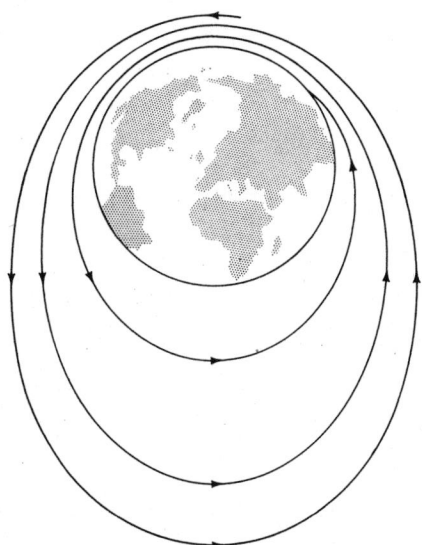

FIG. 24.   Orbit of a Satellite Spiraling Back to Earth

zontally from a rocket at BURNOUT. If a suitable margin has been allowed, its velocity at this instant slightly exceeds the required ORBITAL VELOCITY. When at the diametrically opposite side of the earth, it will be at a greater altitude. It is then at APOGEE; its position at burnout (to which it returns if there is no air resistance) is PERIGEE. If, on returning toward perigee, it encounters appreciable air resistance, its perigee altitude will be slightly less than the original burnout altitude, due to slowing down by drag. Its second apogee altitude will be considerably less than its first. The ellipse will decrease in size and become a spiral; finally the satellite will plunge to the earth or burn up due to friction when it reaches the denser lower atmosphere. To avoid orbital decay, the satellite should be ejected at burnout horizontally at an altitude exceeding 300 miles, approximately.

orbital glider. A BOOST-GLIDE vehicle which, by achieving sufficient velocity and altitude, orbits the earth a pre-determined number of times before returning to the surface.

orbital velocity. This term is used in two senses: 1) The velocity that a satellite (or planet) has at any point of its path, measured along the path and assuming the planet (or sun) around which the aforesaid satellite (or planet) is revolving to be at rest. For a circular orbit, orbital velocity is constant. For an elliptical, non-circular orbit, orbital velocity varies, being minimum at apogee, maximum at perigee. (*See also* SATELLITE.) 2) The minimum velocity that a body projected above the earth, moon, or any planet must have at the initial point of a ballistic path in order that the gravitational field acting on the body will cause it to describe an elliptical orbit that does not intersect the planet's surface. When this condition is realized, the body will return to the initial point and traverse the same orbit indefinitely, provided that the initial point is more than about 300 miles in altitude. (Otherwise air resistance will slow down the body and cause it to fall.)

The most familiar example of orbital velocity used in the second sense is a satellite powered by a rocket. At the instant of BURNOUT, the ballistic path begins. At that instant, the satellite's velocity must exceed the value of orbital velocity *at that point*. This velocity is a function of the earth's gravity, the vehicle's altitude, and the direction of motion.

Orbital velocity decreases with altitude. If the satellite is projected, at burnout, horizontally at exactly orbital velocity, its path will be circular. For a circular orbit round the earth:

$$\text{orbital velocity} = \sqrt{g'R'},$$

where

g' acceleration due to gravity at the initial point of the orbit

R' distance of the initial point from the center of the earth.

$$\text{orbital velocity} = 5\sqrt{\frac{4000}{4000 + h}} \text{ miles/sec,}$$

where h = altitude of initial point in miles.

Orbital velocity (for a circular orbit) at any point equals $\dfrac{1}{\sqrt{2}} \times$ escape velocity at that point.

Figure 25 shows the circular path of a satellite projected horizontally at exactly orbital velocity, such that:

$$V^2 = g'R'$$

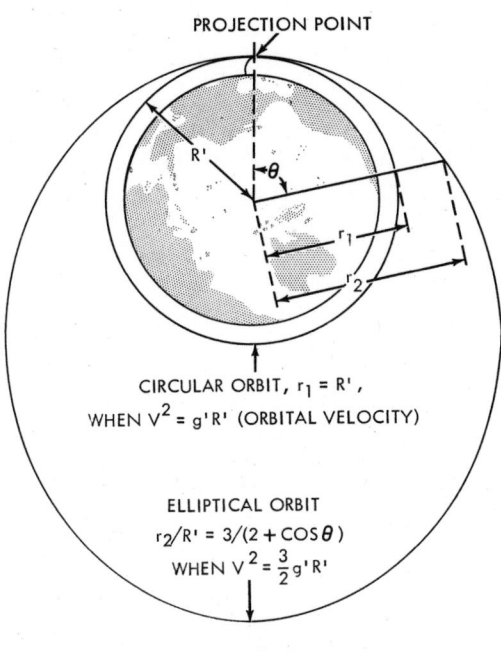

PROJECTION POINT

CIRCULAR ORBIT, $r_1 = R'$,
WHEN $V^2 = g'R'$ (ORBITAL VELOCITY)

ELLIPTICAL ORBIT
$r_2/R' = 3/(2 + \cos\theta)$
WHEN $V^2 = \frac{3}{2}g'R'$

NOTES
V = VELOCITY AT PROJECTION POINT

g' = ACCELERATION DUE TO GRAVITY
AT PROJECTION POINT

FIG. 25.   Circular and Elliptical Orbits of a Satellite

where V = velocity at projection point. At 400 miles altitude, V equals about 4.7 miles/second. The polar equation of the path is

$$r_1 = R',$$

where r_1 = radius vector.

If the satellite is projected at a higher velocity than orbital velocity, its path is elliptical. Figure O-2 shows the elliptical path of a satellite projected horizontally (from the same point as that shown for the satellite taking the circular path) at a velocity slightly higher than orbital velocity, such that:

$$V^2 = \frac{3}{2} g' R'.$$

At 400 miles altitude, V equals about 5.7 miles/second. The polar equation of the path is

$$\frac{r_2}{R'} = \frac{3}{2 + \cos \theta},$$

where

r_2 = radius vector

θ = angle between radius vector and line to projection point.

Orbital velocity also depends on the radius and density of the planet or moon around which the orbit is described. For the moon it would be less, for Jupiter greater than for the earth (considering orbital velocity at the surface).

orbit, braking. A path described by a space vehicle about the earth, or another celestial body with an atmosphere, preparatory to landing, consisting of a series of successively smaller ellipses. In each ellipse, the vehicle dives into the atmosphere, which reduces its speed, then out again, to cool off. Each ellipse, being smaller than the previous one, brings the vehicle into successively denser atmosphere and for a longer period. Thus braking is achieved without over-expenditure of fuel.

orbiter. An orbital rocket or artificial satellite.

orbit, polar. Orbit for an artificial satellite crossing the North and South Poles. Such an orbit permits the satellite to scan all points on the earth's surface.

orbits, circular, mechanics of. A satellite, whether natural or artificial, flies around its parent planet in an orbit that is close to a Kepler ellipse, as conditioned by its own velocity and direction at any point and the planet's gravitational field. Deviations from this ellipse due to the satellite's mass, the gravitational effects of the sun or other planets, or relativistic mechanics, are small. (For the mathematics of a non-circular orbit, reference may be made to any textbook on the dynamics of a particle.) A circular orbit (most natural and some artificial satellite orbits are nearly circular) is more easily described because it obeys the law:

$$\text{centrifugal force} = \text{gravitational force.} \tag{1}$$

These quantities are constant, for circular orbits.

Equation 1 may be written:

$$\frac{mV^2}{r} = \frac{GMm}{r^2}, \tag{2}$$

where

      m = mass of satellite
      M = mass of planet
      V = velocity of satellite
      r = radius of orbit
      G = gravitational constant

This reduces to:

$$V = \sqrt{\frac{GM}{r}}. \tag{3}$$

Thus the satellite's orbital velocity is inversely proportional to the square root of its distance from the center of the earth. From equation 3 it follows that

$$T = \frac{2\pi}{\sqrt{GM}} r^{3/2} \tag{4}$$

where T = time of rotation. Thus time of rotation is proportional to the 3/2th power of distance from the earth's center.

At the surface of the earth (neglecting air resistance), orbital velocity is about 5 miles/second and time of rotation about 83 minutes. At greater altitudes:

$$V = 5 \sqrt{\frac{4000}{4000 + h}} \text{ miles/second (approximately)} \tag{5}$$

$$T = 83 \left(\frac{4000 + h}{4000}\right)^{3/2} \text{ minutes (approximately)} \tag{6}$$

where h = altitude in miles.

In non-circular orbits, V varies, being greatest at perigee (least altitude) and least at apogee (greatest altitude). T can be computed from altitudes at perigee and apogee but the equation is complex.

(*See also* ORBITAL DECAY.)

P

pad. *See* LAUNCH PAD.

parabola of escape. Path of a space vehicle moving at exactly escape velocity at every point along its path. If velocity is decreased, the path becomes an ellipse; if increased, a hyperbola. (*See* figure 7.)

parsec. A unit of length. One parsec is the distance at which the radius of the earth's orbit subtends one second of arc. Thus, from a star n parsecs away the earth's radius subtends $1/n$ second. Likewise, as seen from the earth, the parallax of the star during half a year would be $1/n$ second. One parsec equals approximately $3\frac{1}{4}$ light years.

passive homing.   *See under* HOMING.

payload.   The weight of that portion of a space vehicle which can be described as "useful cargo," such as instruments, personnel, etc.

Peenemunde.   German World War II rocket development center on the banks of the Baltic Sea where the V-1 and V-2 rockets are developed and test-fired.

Pelican.   Army rocket. One of first two U.S.A. operational missiles. Used in World War II.

perigee.   The point of a satellite's orbit around the earth where it is closest to the earth.

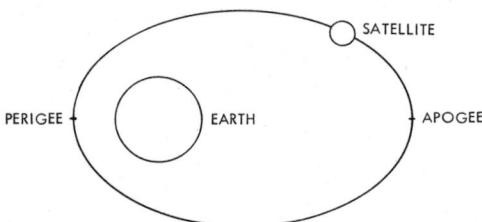

FIG. 26.   Perigee and Apogee

perihelion.   The point of a planet's orbit around the sun where it is closest to the sun.

Pershing.   Army surface-to-surface ballistic missile. Two-stage rocket with solid propellant. One-megaton nuclear warhead. Length: first stage, 30 feet; second stage, somewhat shorter.

perturbation.   The influence of gravitational attraction of one body upon the orbit of another.

Petrel.   Navy air-to-underwater homing turbojet missile. Range: 50 miles. Weight: 3800 pounds. Length: 24 feet.

photo engine.   A projected species of rocket engine using a stream of light rays (photons) to give thrust. Accelerations obtained would be minute.

photon sail.   A proposed means of space travel. The space ship is provided with a sail of some very thin, highly polished material, of the order of a mile in diameter. The sail would move under the action of the pressure of light from the sun (photons) and carry the space ship through space with an accelerated motion. (*See also* SPACE FLIGHT.)

With an aluminized plastic sail 0.1 mil thick, about ½-km square (so as to have a mass of one ton—equal to the assumed mass of the ship), an acceleration of $1.6 \times 10^{-4} \times$ that of gravity would be obtained. Progress would only be possible far from any planet, and in practically zero gravitational field, and could only be in a straight line away from the sun.

Pied Piper.   Air Force code name for an unmanned advanced RECONNAISSANCE SATELLITE. It is designed to carry television and photographic cameras, infrared spotters, and radar-scanner systems. Its orbit is to lie between 300 and 1000 miles altitudes.

pilot-astronaut.   Pilot of a SPACE VEHICLE.

Pioneer.   A class of lunar probe rockets, designed to orbit the moon.

—*Pioneer I.*   Pioneer I was fired on October 11, 1958. It reached an altitude of 80,000 miles and then returned to earth. It was equipped to observe the back of the moon in infrared light, among other projects.

—*Pioneer II.*   Pioneer II, further development of Pioneer I, also failed to reach the moon.

—*Pioneer III.*   Pioneer III, further development of Pioneers I and II, also failed to reach the moon. It reached a height of 66,654 miles, obtaining new and voluminous data on the radiation belt by means of Geiger counters.

—*Pioneer IV.*   Pioneer IV was the first successful U.S.A. lunar probe and sun satellite. *See* SATELLITE, ARTIFICIAL.

plasma.   A fourth state of matter in which atomic nuclear protons are separated from electrons. Used in PLASMA PINCH and PLASMA JET.

plasma jet.   A type of arc, using PLASMA, giving temperatures up to 26,500 degrees Fahrenheit. Currently being used to fabricate solid-propellant rocket nozzles, and to coat experimental nose cones with tungsten and other refractory materials.

plasma pinch.   An effect expected to provide controlled nuclear fusion. The two basic objectives are:

1. To raise a stream of plasma (generally deuterium nuclei separated from electrons) to temperatures of the order of 300 million degrees Kelvin. This has not yet been achieved.

2. To confine and stabilize the plasma to prevent contamination and/or loss of heat due to contact with the container walls, and also the destruction of the walls. It is then proposed to use the heated, high-velocity stream to bombard deuterium atoms, possibly leading to ATOMIC FUSION.

These objectives (except for the extremely high temperatures, and fusion) have been partially realized by using the "pinch effect." Electric current is passed through the stream of plasma; a magnetic field ("magnetic bottle") squeezes the plasma into a smaller diameter, separating it from the walls and further raising its temperature. Alternatively, as in the ASTRON project, the magnetic bottle is produced by a cylinder of electrons rotating at velocities approaching that of light. Heating the plasma may be achieved by passing a high electrical current through it, by surrounding it with a sheath of extremely high-velocity electrons (which also help to confine it), or by "magnetic pumping." The last-named device makes use of cyclotron resonance. A radio-frequency field alternately compresses and expands the gas.

An apparatus used to produce plasma pinch at Project Matterhorn is called a "STELLERATOR."

When controlled fusion has been realized, it is hoped to use the released energy in the form of kinetic energy of a rocket propellant. Exhaust velocities are expected to far exceed those obtainable at present. This, for a given mass ratio, would permit higher rocket velocities and reduce the time of space journeys.

Reference material:

"Zero Infinity", *Aircraft and Missiles Manufacturing*, December 1958, p. 53.
Philip G. Klass, *Aviation Week*, September 29, 1958, p. 39.
John M. Carroll, *Electronics*, December 19, 1958, p. 75.
S. A. Colgate and H. P. Furth, *Science*, August 15, 1958, p. 337.

Plato.   Army surface-to-air anti-missile missile. Now in the planning stage, Plato is an improved version of the NIKE-ZEUS.

Pluto.   Ninth planet of the solar system.

Polaris.   Navy IRBM. Fired from ships or submerged submarines and capable of carrying a nuclear warhead. Smaller than other IRBM's, a sizable number can be carried in a single submarine. The missile is carried aboard in an individual container also containing compressed air which forces the missile to the surface, at which point the rocket engines fire.

polar orbit.   *See* ORBIT, POLAR.

powder.   A solid PROPELLANT.

precession.   An effect manifested by a rotating body when a torque is applied to it in such a way as to tend to change the direction of its axis of rotation. If the speed of rotation and the magnitude of the applied torque are constant, the axis, in general, slowly describes a cone. The effect of gravity on a top is an example.

If the rotating body is symmetrical and its motion unconstrained, and if the torque on its spin axis is at right angles to that axis, the axis of precession will be perpendicular to both spin axis and torque axis. The period of precession is then given by

$$T_p = \frac{4\pi^2 I_s}{QT_s},$$

where

I_s = moment of inertia
T_s = period of spin
Q = torque

The precession of the earth's axis is another case in point. Owing to its having a greater diameter at the equator than along its axis of rotation, the gravitational attraction of the sun and moon tend to pull its axis into the plane of the ecliptic. This causes the axis to describe a cone in space, the period of precession being about 25,000 years.

Conversely, if the body is constrained into rotation at constant speed about an axis perpendicular to the spin axis, a *precession torque* is produced about an axis perpendicular to both axes. The torque is proportional to both the rates of rotation and causes angular acceleration *if unrestrained*. This principle is utilized in RATE GYROS.

The term precession is also applied to the slow rotation of perihelion and aphelion of a planet's orbit around the sun. This phenomenon is accounted for by Einstein's General Theory of Relativity.

pressure suit.   Also called "space suit." A suit designed to protect a passenger abroad a SPACE SHIP from the effects of outer space, primarily vacuum; also cold, and solar and other radiation. Its principal use would be at such times as the passenger was temporarily obliged to leave the ship, either during flight or (say) on the surface of the moon. A pressure suit is airtight and contains air regulated to normal pressure; it is connected with air or oxygen cylinders carried on the passenger's back, and includes a plastic transparent helmet. Another requisite is temperature-conditioning of the enclosed air, and heat insulation. Pressure suits have already been designed and tested on personnel in evacuated chambers.

It has been suggested that during takeoff the passenger should wear an "immersion suit," with water filling the space between the suit and the passenger's body. This, it is alleged, would prevent the high accelerations from causing any high blood displacements.

probe.   An exploratory rocket flight. *See* LUNAR PROBE and SPACE PROBE.

program.   A prescribed series of events in a normal missile flight. These events may be actuated by such things as clock mechanisms, pressure transducers, ACCELEROMETERS, RATE GYROS, etc.

Project Farside. Air Force program to send a rocket to the moon.

Project Matterhorn. *See* STELLERATOR.

Project Mercury. NASA man-in-space project. Objective: to place a *manned* space capsule in orbit around the earth and recover the capsule after one or more revolutions.

Project Muskrat. U.S. Naval Research Laboratory cosmic ray research program.

Project Score. Signal Communication by Orbiting Relay Equipment. An experiment in surface-to-surface communication via the ATLAS satellite. Relay equipment, satellite-borne, stores information received from one point on earth and releases it to another point when triggered. It has been proposed that the equipment should only receive coded interrogation, in order to prevent its being "overworked" by unfriendly agencies.

Project Scout. NASA low-cost launching rocket project. (*See also* SCOUT.)

Project Stratoscope. Office of Naval Research program for high-altitude photography. An altitude of 20 miles has already been achieved. It is planned to use a 36-inch telescope at an altitude above atmospheric interference with visibility and, eventually, construct a satellite observatory with a 500-mile perigee.

Project Vanguard. *See* OPERATION VANGUARD.

propellant. The fuel and associated substances for combustion, used in generating the thrust for a rocket due to the expansion of combustion products through the exhaust nozzle. Propellants are of two types: liquid and solid.

Until recently, liquid propellants have predominated, as being easier to manufacture. Some commonly used fuels are kerosene, gasoline, alcohol, and hydrazine; some commonly used oxidants are oxygen, hydrogen peroxide, nitric acid, and fluorine. Liquid propellants, too, have certain advantages: a high SPECIFIC IMPULSE and a THRUST which can be varied.

However, solid propellants are now coming to the fore. Their values of specific impulse, though lower than that of the liquid propellants, is catching up rapidly. Furthermore, they do not evaporate or deteriorate in storage; they need no pumps, pipes, turbines, auxiliary gas generators, and control gears; and they permit far quicker countdown. Solid propellants can consist of a substance such as cordite, which contains the oxygen for combustion within its own nitrocellulose and nitroglycerin molecules. More recent solids are mixtures of fuels and oxidizers held together with a resinous binder. The fuel is often a ground-up organic salt; the oxidizer may be the binder itself.

The latest development in propellants is the use of EXOTIC FUELS, by means of which higher specific impulses are obtained than with other fuels now in use.

—bipropellant. A rocket propellant consisting of two unmixed chemicals fed to the combustion chamber separately.

—composite propellant. A propellant with separate fuel and oxidizer.

—diergolic propellant. Not HYPERGOLIC. A propellant whose fuel and oxidizer do not react spontaneously but require an auxiliary ignition system.

—double-base propellant. A solid propellant consisting of gelatinized colloidal mixtures of nitrocellulose and nitroglycerin, with the addition of certain stabilizers.

—heterogeneous propellant. COMPOSITE PROPELLANT.

—homogeneous propellant. A solid propellant whose fuel and oxidizer form a single, or colloidal entity, *e.g.* cordite, ballistite.

—hypergolic propellant. A propellant which ignites spontaneously on mixing.

—monopropellant. A single liquid capable of complete oxidation reaction within itself.

—restricted propellant. A solid propellant system where combustion takes place perpendicular to the longitudinal axis of the GRAIN. Often termed "end burner."

—trapped propellant. In a liquid propellant, that residual in the fuel feed lines which cannot be used because of inadequate suction head.

—unrestricted propellant. A solid propellant where combustion takes place on more than one planar surface.

propellant utilization system. An automatic electromechanical system installed on very large ballistic missiles to control the mixture ratio of oxidizer to fuel in liquid propellants as they are consumed in firing.

propjet. *See* TURBOPROP.

proportional-navigation guidance. *See* GUIDANCE, MISSILE.

PU system. PROPELLANT UTILIZATION SYSTEM.

pulse jet. A form of RAMJET consisting of a large metal tube with a valve at the forward end. Fuel ignited behind the valve develops a pressure that closes the valve and causes a jet impulse at the rear exit nozzle. The valve is then opened by the reduced pressure within the tube, and a fresh charge of air is admitted for the next firing impulses. Example: German V-1.

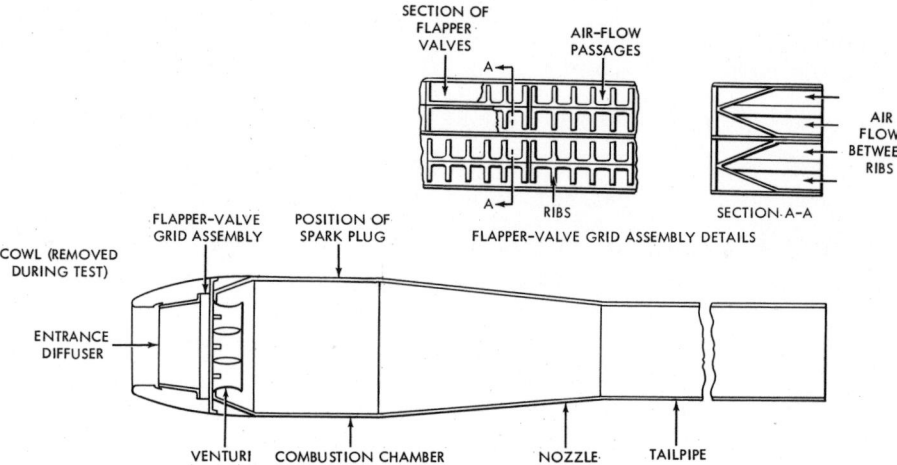

FIG. 27. Pulse Jet   (Van Nostrand's Scientific Encyclopedia, D. Van Nostrand Company, Inc.)

pursuit course. A flight course in which the missile is continuously moving toward the present position of the target.

pursuit-course guidance. *See under* GUIDANCE, MISSILE.

Q

Quail. Air Force air-to-surface cruise missile. (Also designated GAM-72.) (*See also* GREEN QUAIL.)

R

radar. Radio detection and range-finding system. A system of detection in which radiant energy of ultra-high or higher frequency is transmitted to and reflected from the object of search back to the transmitting source. The time delay between the transmitted and echo signals indicates the distance of the object of search from the transmitting source. The radiant energy is generally pulsed, but in special forms of radar (Doppler and f-m) it may be continuous-wave.

Figure 28 shows the major components of a basic radar system. These are:

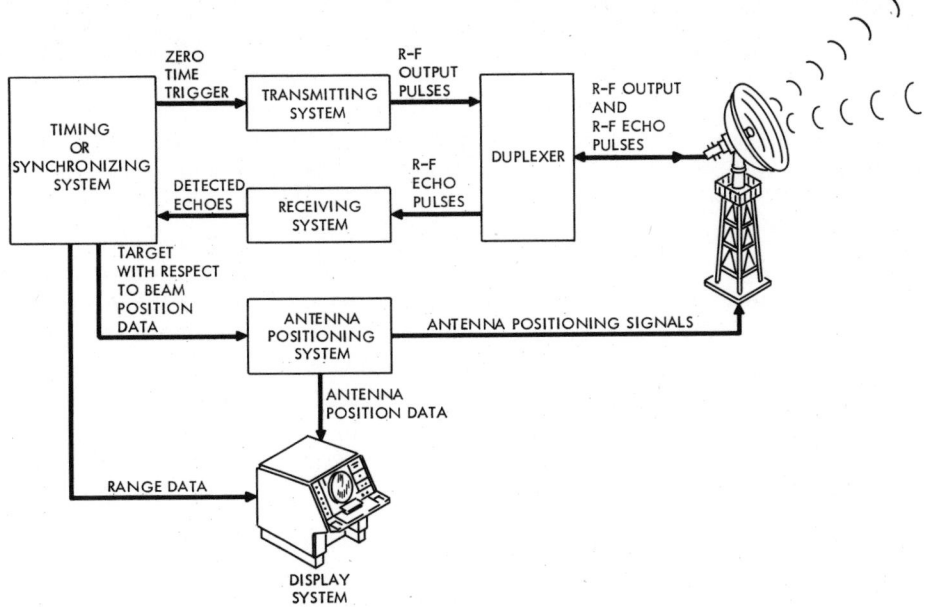

FIG. 28.   Basic Radar System

1. Timing and synchronizing system. Establishes the repetition rate of out-going pulses, measures the time delay preceding each corresponding echo pulse, and converts the time delay into usable range data. Also generates the start of the display system oscilloscope sweep. Also interprets echo pulse information so as to derive data on target range and position with respect to the transmitted r-f beam.

2. Transmitting system. When triggered by the synchronizing system, the transmitter system develops a high-power r-f pulse for transmission by the antenna.

3. Receiving system. Receives from the antenna, amplifies, and detects the very weak r-f echo pulse reflected from the target and applies it to the timing and synchronizing system.

4. Antenna. Radiates pulses in a polarized pencil beam to the target and receives echo pulses from the target. Positions the beam in space in accordance with signals from the antenna positioning system.

5. Duplexer. Permits use of a single antenna for the transmission of high-powered pulses and the reception of weak echo pulses.

6. Antenna positioning system. Permits manual or automatic positioning of the antenna in accordance with input signals.

7. Display system. Presents visual presentations in the form of dial or cathode-ray tube displays of target range and position angle.

Radar has several applications in the field of missiles, as discussed below.

1. Tracking. The antenna is automatically positioned for maximum echo signal. Azimuth and elevation of antenna are continuously recorded to provide a plot of target position. Missile range is also tracked and recorded.

2. Search. The antenna is manually positioned and programmed to cover a sector of space until an echo is obtained and target position noted. After the target is acquired, automatic lockon and tracking may begin.

3. Fire control. The radar (one or more systems may be used) tracks the target and feeds target range and position data to a computer. The computer computes required lead angles and makes the necessary ballistic corrections required to position a gun or missile so that the target can be intercepted.

4. Homing. The antenna axis is made rigid with the missile axis; the radar feeds missile and target position signals to the missile flight control system so that the entire missile is maneuvered to position the antenna beam squarely on the target. *See also* BEAM GUIDANCE *under* GUIDANCE, MISSILE.

radar tracker. A radar system that illuminates a target with r-f energy and uses the reflected energy to maintain the antenna on the target. The position of the antenna describes the azimuth and elevation of the target (angular tracking). A servo system activated by the transit time of the r-f energy permits range tracking. *See* RADAR.

radiation belt. The radiation belt probed by Pioneer III, using Geiger counters, on its flight to 66,654 miles altitude. Considered to be caused by the trapping of particles from the sun, etc, by the earth's magnetic field. (*See* figure 29.)

This belt is also called the "Van Allen layer", after Professor James A. Van Allen, in charge of Explorer instrumentation. (The belt was first discovered by means of the satellite Explorer I and later confirmed by Explorer III.) The belt actually consists of two layers:

1. A layer at 1400-3400 miles altitude, at low geo-magnetic latitudes.

2. A second layer at 8000-12,000 miles altitude, up to perhaps 50 or 60 degrees geo-magnetic latitude.

Maximum radiation for both layers is 10 roentgens/hour if due to electrons, 100 roentgens/hour if due to protons, at 2400 miles and 10,000 miles altitude, respectively.

Minimum radiation in the buffer zone is 0.3 roentgen/hour, at 6000 miles altitude. (The maximum safe dosage recommended by the AEC is 0.3 roentgen/week.) At 25,000 miles, radiation has fallen to 1/1000 peak value. Beyond 36,000 miles, radiation appears to remain constant at 1/10,000 peak value. This indicates a sharp drop in the earth's magnetic field.

radio telescope. An extremely sensitive radio receiver and highly directional antenna system used to explore the heavens by detecting the electro-

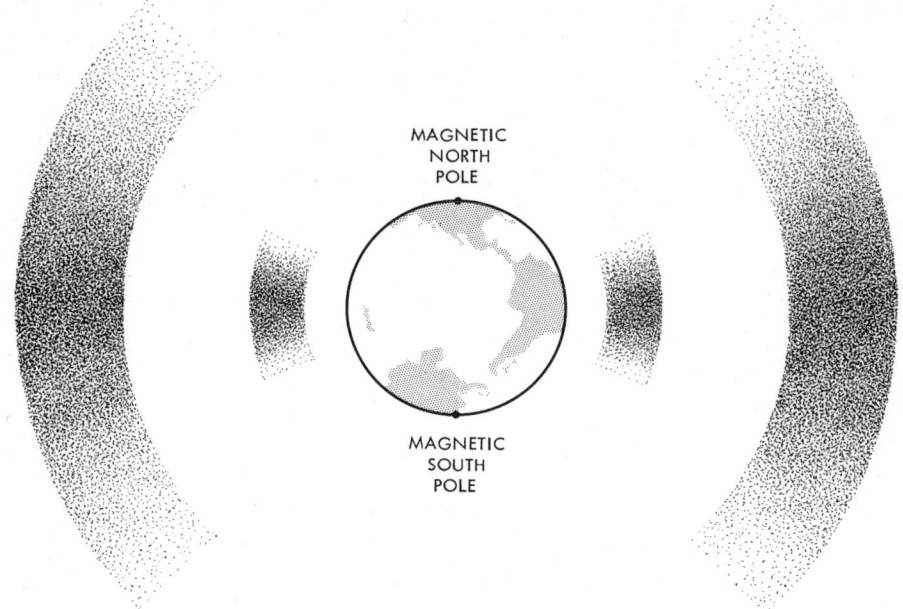

Fɪɢ. 29. Layers of the Radiation Belt

magnetic radiation of the stars. Radio telescopes are also used to track space probe rockets.

radome. A protective covering for an operating radar antenna. On airborne radar systems, the radome is shaped to eliminate undesirable aerodynamic characteristics.

ram drag. *See* Dʀᴀɢ, ʀᴀᴍ.

ramjet. A type of missile or aircraft with no rotating parts, deriving its velocity from the intake of air at the forward end, combustion of fuel, and ejection of combustion products at the rear end. (*See* Aᴛʜᴏᴅʏᴅ and Pᴜʟsᴇ ᴊᴇᴛ.)

ramrocket. A combination of ᴀᴛʜᴏᴅʏᴅ ʀᴀᴍᴊᴇᴛ with rocket engines. One or more rocket engines are mounted inside the ramjet so that they act both as igniters and as fuel injectors. Secondary fuel injection is also used. The rocket engines augment the ramjet thrust both by direct rocket thrust and entrainment of more air than the simple ramjet can handle; they also provide a static thrust. Unlike the ramjet, the ramrocket can start from rest.

Rascal. Air Force air-to-surface guided rocket missile. Radar command guidance. Liquid propellant engine, 12,000 pounds thrust. Range: over 100 miles at velocity of Mach 1.5. (Also designated GAM-63.)

Rat. Navy anti-submarine rocket-assisted guided torpedo. Destroyer-launched or air-launched. Solid-propellant booster. Rocket separates when missile enters water. Missile then starts circling search until homing device makes contact. Range previously determined by sonar at destroyer.

rate gyro. A gyro which spins in such a manner that its precessional torque is proportional to the rate of rotation of the entire gyro about a given axis.

ratio, mass. *See* MASS RATIO.

ratio, velocity. *See* VELOCITY RATIO.

RATO unit. Rocket-assisted-takeoff unit. A BOOSTER rocket.

Raven. Navy air-to-surface missile. Hot-gas generator propulsion system.

reaction engine. An engine that derives thrust by expelling a stream of moving particles. *See* ROCKET.

reaction motor. *See* REACTION ENGINE.

reaction time. The interval of time between command to launch and actual launch.

reactor, nuclear. An apparatus in which NUCLEAR FISSION can be sustained in a self-supporting chain reaction. The term is usually applied to systems in which the reaction proceeds at a controlled rate. The reactor includes fissionable material such as uranium or plutonium, reflector (usually) to conserve escaping neutrons, provision for heat removal, and measuring and control elements. Fusion reactors have not yet been achieved but research is proceeding as to their possibility. (*See also* ATOMIC ENERGY and PLASMA PINCH.)

—*high-flux reactor.* A nuclear reactor operating at a high rate of fission per unit volume and therefore with high neutron flux.

—*porous reactor.* A nuclear reactor composed of a porous material with coolant or fluid fuel flowing through the pores.

—*thermal reactor.* A nuclear reactor in which fission is induced primarily by neutrons of energy such that they are in substantial thermal equilibrium with the core material.

reconnaissance satellite. *See under* SATELLITE, ARTIFICIAL.

recovery. The act of recovering a missile after it has completed the journey to its target. This is made possible by signals transmitted from a package contained by the missile and (generally) ejected by it before falling to the ground or into the sea. These signals may consist of flares, radio waves, or underwater sonic waves.

recovery package. An instrumentation package or data capsule carried by a missile that is designed to survive RE-ENTRY and/or terminal impact. The package is (generally) ejected by the missile at the end of its journey, and transmits signals indicating the locality of the package so that it may be recovered. *See* RECOVERY.

Redstone. Army surface-to-surface rocket missile. Length: 62 feet. Range: 200-300 miles. Liquid propellant. Thrust: 75,000 pounds.

re-entry. 1. The return of the NOSE CONE of a ballistic missile into the earth's atmosphere after completing the major portion of its ballistic path, *i.e.* the portion so high above the earth as to be, virtually, in a vacuum. Nose cone re-entry is one of the more serious problems connected with ballistic missiles, because the nose cone is traveling at such a high velocity that it is liable to be burnt up by atmospheric friction unless special precautions are taken. (In the recent 6500-mile flight of an Atlas, re-entry was successfully accomplished.) In certain ballistic missiles now being considered, this difficulty may be partly overcome by supplying the nose cone with an extra set of rocket engines designed to slow it up immediately prior to re-entry, and possibly provide last-minute guidance.

2. The return of an ARTIFICIAL SATELLITE into the earth's atmosphere after completing one or, more generally, a number of revolutions around the earth. Satellite re-entry is of two kinds, due to failure and to plan, respectively. Re-entry due to failure occurs when the satellite has been projected at burnout with insufficient velocity or in the wrong direction. (*See* ORBITAL DECAY.) Re-entry due to plan occurs when a satellite, after performing a required number of successful orbits, is slowed down by RETRO-ROCKETS, which it carries for this purpose and which are (presumably) set off by a ground signal. A manned satellite or SPACE CAPSULE, as planned at present, will carry a drag parachute which will open after the retrorockets have sufficiently slowed the vehicle down. Also, it will be provided with an inflatable bag to cushion a landing on the ground or provide buoyancy for a landing on the water. The retrorockets, heat shield, and heat sink are jettisoned prior to the opening of the parachute. (*See* figure 30.)

re-entry vehicle. 1. Air Force designation for the nose cone of an ICBM or IRBM.

2. Any space vehicle that returns to the earth's atmosphere.

reflector, confusion. *See* CONFUSION REFLECTOR.

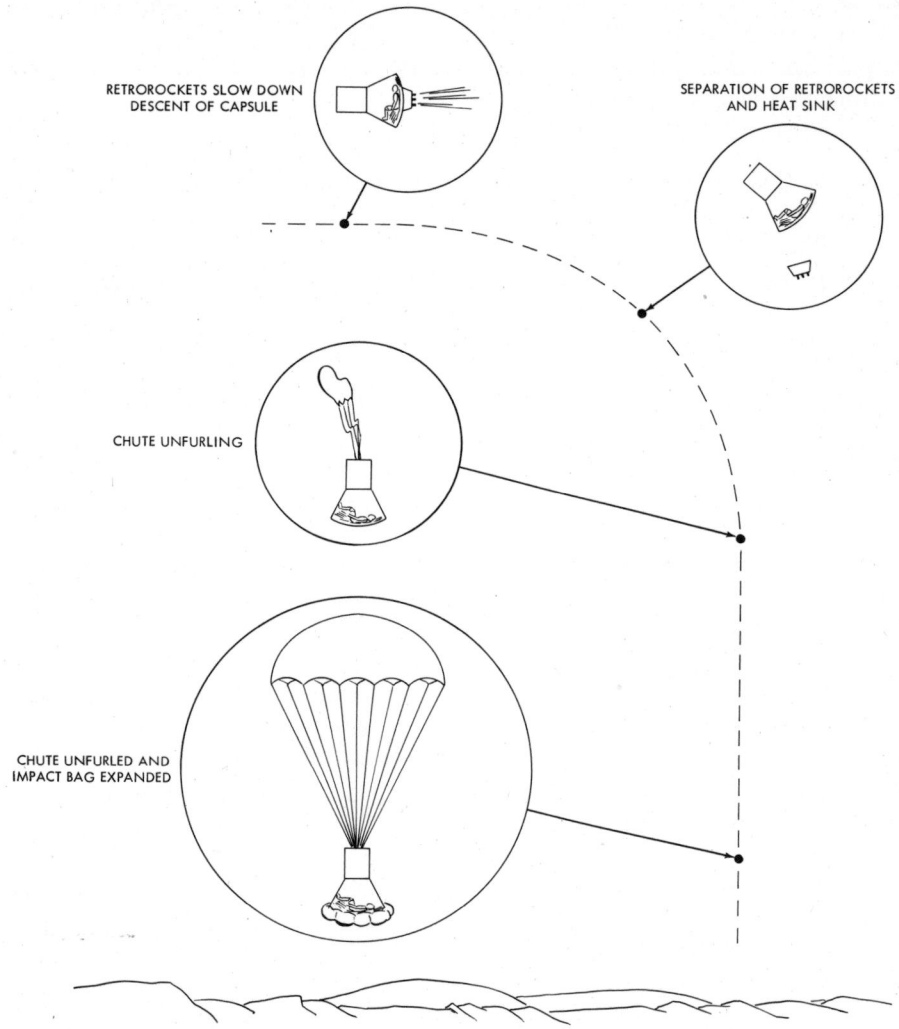

RETROROCKETS SLOW DOWN
DESCENT OF CAPSULE

SEPARATION OF RETROROCKETS
AND HEAT SINK

CHUTE UNFURLING

CHUTE UNFURLED AND
IMPACT BAG EXPANDED

FIG. 30. Slow-Down of a Space Capsule During Re-entry

Regulus. Navy class of surface-to-surface guided missiles.

—*Regulus I*. Launched from a short rail launcher by two solid-propellant jato rocket boosters. To be launched by Marines from surfaced submarines against land targets.

—*Regulus II*. Hypersonic. Launched from submarines, aircraft carriers, cruisers, and shore bases. Carries a J79 turbojet engine. Can deliver a nuclear warhead. Range: 1000 miles. Altitude: over 60,000 feet. Speed: over twice the speed of sound.

relativity. A theory developed by Albert Einstein, first considered revolutionary but now generally accepted. It includes: "Special Theory of Relativity" (1905), "General Theory of Relativity" (1915), and subsequent recent extensions, notably the Unified Field Theorem.

The special theory is based on the hypothesis that the velocity of light is the same when measured by any one of a set of observers moving with constant relative velocity. This theory was originally evolved to account for the failure of all attempts to detect drift of the earth through the "ether."

Some postulates of the special theory are:

1. Space cannot be considered without time, nor time without space. Space and time must be considered in respect to each other in a four-dimensional continuum. For instance: it is meaningless to specify *where* an event occurs without also specifying *when*, and vice versa. There is no such thing as absolute velocity (or, as the expression used to be, velocity relative to the ether). There is only relative velocity between different objects.

2. If one observer is moving with respect to another observer, they will form different estimates of the length or mass of an object, or of the time elapsing between two events.

3. Matter and energy are not each indestructible, as previously supposed, but can be converted into one another according to the transformation law: $E = mc^2$, where E = energy in ergs, m = mass in grams, c = velocity of light in cm/sec (3×10^{10}).

Apart from its success in accounting for the results of the ether-drift (Michelson and Morley) experiment, the special theory has received special note from its prediction of the release of atomic energy. It also predicts time dilatation.

The general theory relates the measurements of observers who are accelerated relative to each other and hence are not in an inertial system. The fundamental postulate is the "principle of equivalence" from which may be deduced the equality of the "inertial mass" and "gravitational mass" of a system. In addition, it is postulated that the equations of mechanics have the same form for all observers, whether accelerated or not. The motion of a system is represented in a four-dimensional, "Riemannian," space-time continuum.

Gravity is not considered an "attraction" in the former sense. The new concept is that space-time is warped by surrounding masses, so that a particle which, if projected into empty space, would follow a straight line actually follows a geodesic of this warped space-time, representing physically the most direct path between any two points. Einstein's equivalence principle makes no distinction between gravitational and centrifugal force.

Two early successes of the general theory were the predictions of:

1. The bending of light in a gravitational field.
2. The PRECESSION of the perihelion of Mercury.

Both these phenomena have since been observed. Recent extensions of the theory of relativity integrate the laws of gravitation and electromagnetism (Unified Field Theorem).

One of the postulates of the general theory is that the rate of a clock is changed by a change in its gravitational scalar potential. This leads to a resolution of the "Clock Paradox." (*See* TIME DILATATION.)

Relativity is primarily a challenge to some of the "absolute" doctrines of the nineteenth century. The consequences of its main postulates have been developed mathematically and have found justification in many physical phenomena.

Relativity is not so much a contradiction of Newtonian mechanics as the statement of a more general law of which Newtonian mechanics is a special case. Newtonian mechanics is still a good approximation, as regards phenomena not involving velocities of the order of the velocity of light.

Relativity has two important applications to rockets and space flight. (*See* TIME DILATATION.)

resojet. A PULSE JET.

resonant burning. Unstable combustion vibration in solid-propellant rocket, resulting in acoustical resonance. Commonly termed "chugging" or "screaming."

retractable launcher. *See under* LAUNCHER.

retrorocket. Rocket engine(s) ejecting from the forward nozzle of a vehicle in order to decelerate the rocket.

RI. Radio inertial guiding. *See* INERTIAL GUIDANCE *under* GUIDANCE, MISSILE.

robot bomb. Generally a surface-to-surface missile directed by autopilot and other automatic device. The German V-1 was an example.

rocket. An apparatus consisting of a case containing a propellant, *i.e.* fuel and reagents, by the combustion of which it may be projected to a height or distance. A rocket takes in no ambient air, and does not use it in any way. A rocket ejects the products of combustion through a nozzle and is thereby projected in the opposite direction by the principle of recoil and conservation of momentum. Thus, the rocket does not need to "push against" air or any other matter. Its forward gain in momentum equals the ejected combustion product's backward gain in momentum. Thus, the rocket is the only missile or space vehicle (outside certain speculations concerning magnetic and gravitational fields) capable of powered flight through a vacuum. (A ballistic missile travels through a vacuum but is not under power for most of its flight.)

The propulsive components of a rocket (fuel, reagents, and associated gear) are referred to as "rocket engines" or "rocket motors." (*See* figure

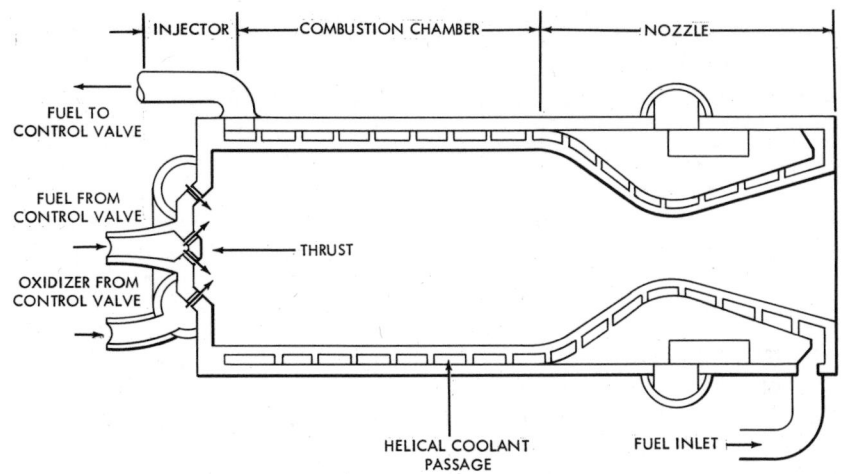

Fɪɢ. 31.   Rocket Engine

31.) At any instant, the rocket accelerates according to the "classic equation":

mass × acceleration = velocity of exhaust × rate of mass loss   (1

As its mass is decreasing, so its acceleration increases. This leads to the equation:

$$\frac{V}{u} = \log_e \frac{M}{m} \qquad (2)$$

where

u = exhaust velocity relative to the rocket
V = rocket velocity at any instant
M = rocket mass at launching
m = rocket mass at instant of velocity V
e = 2.71828

That is to say:

velocity ratio = natural log of mass ratio   (3)

or

mass ratio = $e^{(velocity\ ratio)}$ (4)

These equations represent a simplification of the general problem and must be modified to deal with actual conditions involving sideways expansion of combustion products after leaving the nozzle, also the effects of the surrounding atmosphere (which is necessarily present during the earlier portions of a flight). Nevertheless, the classic equation is qualitatively correct and can be used for rough predictions on the behavior of rockets in general.

If a rocket is coasting with its engines off, and rocket engines are started up with forward ejection, the rocket will correspondingly decelerate. This principle is expected to be made use of in: 1) Moon landings, where the rocket engine will act as a brake (essential since the moon has no atmosphere); 2) manned satellites or ballistic missiles, where its brake will reduce the re-entry problem.

If it is desired to attain a velocity much in excess of exhaust velocity, it follows from equation 4 that a very large mass ratio will be required, *i.e.* a very small mass at burnout compared to the original mass.

Higher velocities can be attained (though at the cost of a greater mass ratio) by driving the rocket in two or more "stages." When the rocket engines of stage 1 are burnt out, stage 2 separates itself from the fuselage of stage 1, which is ejected backward and jettisoned. Stage 2 then starts up its own rocket engines. And so on. All earth satellites to date have been launched by multi-stage rockets. (In certain multi-stage rockets, the engines of the successive stages are all fired at the start.) (*See* figure 32.)

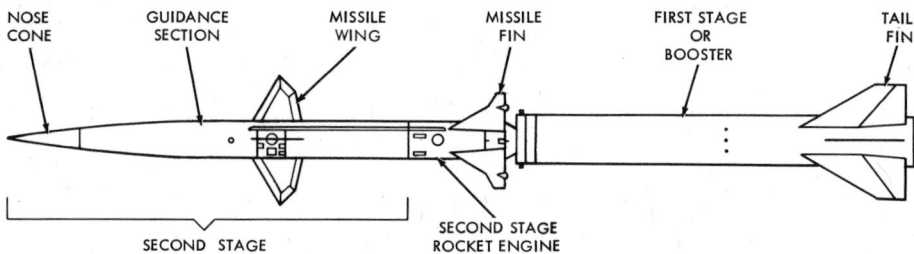

FIG. 32. Component Parts of a Rocket (Missiles and Rockets, American Aviation Publications, July 28, 1958)

However, the greatest hope for rockets lies in the improvement of fuels, resulting in a higher exhaust velocity. A measure of rocket merit, termed "specific impulse," is defined as: number of pounds of thrust per pound of fuel liberated per second. This can readily be shown to equal $\dfrac{1}{g} \times$ exhaust velocity, where g = acceleration due to gravity = 32.2 feet/sec^2:

thrust in poundals = mass $\times$ acceleration

= exhaust velocity $\times$ rate of mass loss in pounds (see equation 1)

$$\frac{\text{thrust in poundals}}{\text{rate of mass loss in lb.}} = \text{exhaust velocity}$$

$$\text{specific impulse} = \frac{\text{thrust in pounds}}{\text{rate of mass loss in pounds}}.$$

$$= \frac{\text{exhaust velocity}}{g}$$

Fuels, to date, are of two varieties: solid and liquid. At present, the best do not give a specific impulse exceeding 300, *i.e.* an exhaust velocity of 9000 ft/sec. In a single-stage rocket, to obtain orbital velocity (about 5 miles/sec), a mass ratio of about 3:1 would be required. To obtain escape velocity (about 7 miles/sec), a mass ratio of about 4.5:1 would be required. Hope is felt in many quarters that great improvements may eventually be brought about by "exotic fuels," especially atomic fuels. (*See* PROPELLANT.) One predicted use of atomic fuels is in the "ion rocket," in which atoms or molecules are ionized, and the ions are boosted to high exhaust velocities. These velocities would reduce fuel consumption to a minimum and, most important of all in space flight, possibly enable a rocket to be powered throughout a space journey.

For, if space flight is to be accomplished with present-day fuels, final burnout will occur very early and most of the flight will be performed in "free fall" and at speeds of only a few miles per second. The crew will endure "weightlessness" and other discomforts for days (in flying to the moon) or for months (in flying to a planet).

One hope for the elimination of such conditions is the possible discovery of atomic fuels that will work on a new, yet to be discovered, scientific principle, *i.e.* the direct conversion of atomic energy into kinetic energy of exhaust without the generation of heat. Exhaust velocity might then be so high that the crew of a space ship could accelerate at 1 *g* for half the journey and decelerate at 1 *g* for the remainder. They would then: 1) experience no weightlessness, and 2) be able to reach the moon in 3½ hours or Mars at opposition in 2 days. Many believe that such fuels will come in the not-too-distant future and it is then that space flight will become a practical reality.

—booster rocket.   *See* BOOSTER.

—brake rocket.   *See* RETROROCKET.

—circumlunar rocket.   Rocket that returns to earth after circling the moon.

—dawn rocket.   A rocket launched at dawn in the direction of the earth's orbital motion. The take-off velocity, *V*, is thereby increased by the earth's orbital velocity (18.5 miles/second). (*See* figure 33.)

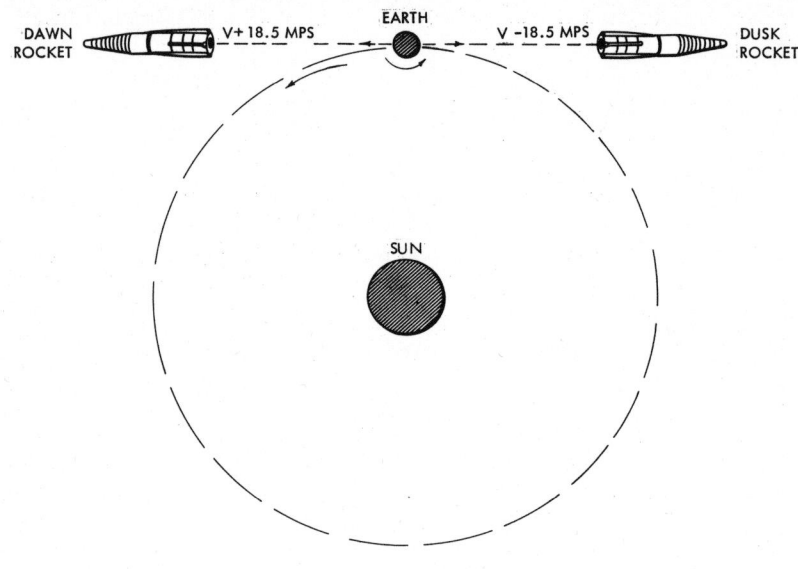

FIG. 33.　Effect of Earth's Rotation on Velocities of Dawn and Dusk Rockets

—dusk rocket.　A rocket launched at dusk in the opposite direction to the earth's orbital motion. The take-off velocity, *V*, is thereby diminished by the earth's orbital velocity (18.5 miles/second). (*See* figure 33.)

—ferry rocket.　The final stage of a space vehicle, used for transporting personnel between the earth and the terminal orbit.

—hybrid rocket.　A solid-propellant rocket using an auxiliary liquid propellant or some other working fluid (*e.g.* air).

—ion rocket.　A rocket powered by atomic fuel in which ions are segregated and boosted to high exhaust velocities. This may be achieved when controlled atomic fusion becomes a reality. (*See* THERMONUCLEAR ENGINE and PLASMA PINCH.)

—landing rocket.　A secondary rocket used for descending to the surface of the moon or a planet while the major space vehicle remains in orbit.

—multi-stage rocket.　A rocket composed of two or more stages, each with its own rocket engine and fuselage. When the first stage is burnt out, its fuselage is ejected backward and jettisoned. A greater velocity ratio can thus be obtained. A tandem missile.

—step rocket.　A multi-stage rocket.

—*sounding rocket.* A rocket launched for data-gathering purposes.

rocket axis. The longitudinal axis of symmetry of a rocket.

rocket engine. *See* Engine, rocket.

rocket sled. A vehicle running on rails and propelled by rocket thrust, used to investigate the effect of high accelerations on the human body for brief periods. The sled used in the latest experiments is provided with bucket brakes that act by scooping up tons of water. The greatest force on the passenger is produced during brake action, *i.e.* is due to deceleration. More than 40 *g*'s (for a period of about one second) have been experienced without lasting damage to the passenger. One result of these experiments has been that Air Force transports now have rearward-facing passenger seats, because it was demonstrated that they have a better chance of surviving crashes that way. It is thought that humans can endure the accelerations involved in attaining orbital or escape velocities, or in re-entry, in present three-stage rocket vehicles.

Rocket sleds are also used to test aircraft equipment for flutter at different speeds.

Rockoon. A rocket hoisted by and launched from a balloon. A pressure-sensitive switch completes the ignition circuit for the rocket when atmospheric pressure is at a desired low level. (*See* figure 34.)

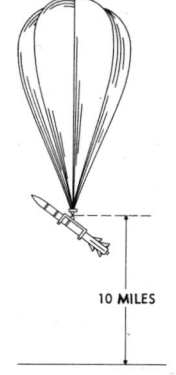

10 MILES

Fig. 34. Rockoon

rope. *See* Window.

ROTI. Recording optical tracking instrument. Equipment for recording missile position by means of two large-aperture telescopes with long focal length.

R/V. Re-entry vehicle.

S

SAC-Mike. Strategic Air Command ballistic missile staff. *Colloq.*

SAGE. Semi-automatic ground environment. Designation for a control center for continental defense of the U.S.A. in an assigned sector. It is planned to have about 40 such installations to cover the country. SAGE evaluates data inputs for all air activity in its sector and initiates appropriate interception action for all unidentified craft. Interception may be by manned aircraft or by missiles such as BOMARC which can be launched directly by command of SAGE.

SAM. Surface-to-air missile.

satellite. An attendant body revolving about a larger one. Up to the last decade, this term has been used almost exclusively to denote a planet's moon, such as our own moon, Mars' Deimos and Phobos, and the numerous moons of the major planets. Since the autumn of 1957, it has also come to mean a man-made body put into orbit around the earth or other solar body. These man-made satellites are called "ARTIFICIAL SATELLITES" or "artificial planets."

satellite, artificial. A man-made body placed in orbit around a sun, planet, or satellite. Usually it carries instruments for recording and transmitting data about conditions on earth and in space. An artificial satellite can record:

1. Ultra-violet, X-ray and corpuscular solar radiation not received at the earth's surface owing to atmospheric absorption.
2. The earth's magnetic field.
3. Intensity of meteoric dust.
4. Cosmic rays.
5. Time measurements, made with a satellite clock, for relativity investigations.

The life of an artificial satellite is limited, not only by atmospheric friction (if the altitude be much under 300 miles) but the gravitational effect of the earth's equatorial bulge. This causes precession and eventual orbital decay. Another possible cause is loss of momentum due to picking up ions in the ionosphere.

It has been proposed, as an aid in tracking artificial satellites, to have the satellite release an inflatable plastic balloon, carrying a nitrogen capsule which, when triggered will explode and fill the balloon. The nitrogen will then be released, lest the balloon should be punctured by a micrometeorite and become self-propelled. The balloon, being in a vacuum, will retain its shape.

(*See also* ORBITS, CIRCULAR, MECHANICS OF and ORBITAL VELOCITY.)

As of March 4, 1959, 12 artificial satellites had been launched successfully, eight by the U.S.A. and four by the USSR. Of these, ten were put into orbit around the earth and two around the sun. They are listed below.

Earth Satellites

Sputnik I (USSR).   Launched October 1957. Weight: 184 pounds. Sphere-shaped, 22.8 inches in diameter. Orbit time: 96 minutes. Speed: 18,000 mph. Maximum height: 560 miles. Minimum height: 125 miles. Burned up January 4, 1958.

Sputnik II (USSR).   Launched November 3, 1957. Weight: 1118 pounds. Cone-shaped, 15 feet long. Orbit time: 103.7 minutes. Speed: 17,800 mph. Maximum height: 1020 miles. Minimum height: 140 miles. Burned up April 14, 1958.

Explorer I (U.S.A.).   Launched Jan. 31, 1958. Weight: 30.8 pounds. Tube-shaped, 80 inches long. Time of orbit: 113.35 minutes. Speed: 19,000 mph. Maximum height: 1509.9 miles. Minimum height: 218.2 miles. Expected stay in orbit: 3 to 5 years.

Vanguard I (U.S.A.).   Launched March 17, 1958. Weight: 3.25 pounds. Sphere-shaped, 6.4 inches in diameter. Orbit time: 134.25 minutes. Speed: 18,365 mph. Maximum height: 2458 miles. Minimum height: 409.1 miles. Expected stay in orbit: at least 200 years.

Explorer III (U.S.A.).   Launched March 26, 1958. Weight: 31 pounds. Tube-shaped, 79 inches long. Orbit time: 115.7 minutes. Speed: 18,000 mph. Maximum height: 2000 miles. Minimum height: 100 miles. Believed burned up in June 1958.

Sputnik III (USSR).   Launched May 15, 1958. Weight: 2925.53 pounds Cone-shaped, 11.8 feet long. Orbit time: 105.21 minutes. Speed: 14,746 mph. Maximum height: 1120 miles. Minimum height: 128 miles.

Explorer IV (U.S.A.).   Launched July 26, 1958. Weight: 38 pounds. Bullet-shaped, 80 inches long. Orbit time: 110 minutes. Maximum height: 1372 miles. Expected stay in orbit: 5 to 10 years.

Atlas (U.S.A.).   Launched December 18, 1958. Weight: 8700 to 8800 pounds. Orbit time: about 100 minutes. Speed: in excess of 17,000 mph. Maximum height: 920 miles. Minimum height: 115 miles. Burned up.

Vanguard II (U.S.A.).   Launched February 17, 1959. Navy meteorological satellite. Carries two photocells which operate in conjunction with a solar battery, an infrared detector, an optical system, and a tape recorder to telemeter weather data back to the earth. Weight: 2½ pounds. Diameter:

20 inches. Maximum height: 1600 miles. Minimum height: 200-300 miles. Expected stay in orbit: several months to a few years.

Discoverer I (U.S.A.). Launched February 28, 1959. First earth satellite designed to go into polar orbit.[1] 19 feet long. Weight: 1300 pounds. Launched

[1] On March 5, 1959, the Defense Department announced that Discoverer I was in orbit. However, two weeks later, a spokesman declared flatly that "we know for sure it wasn't up there." (*New York Times,* March 18, 1959.)

by two-stage rocket, the first stage being a Thor IRBM, the second stage a cylinder containing a Hustler rocket engine. Carries 44 pounds of instruments. Maximum height: 450 miles. Minimum height: 150 miles. Orbital time: 95.5 minutes. Expected stay in orbit: over 30 days. Believed burned up between March 5 and March 18, 1959.

Sun Satellites

Lunik (USSR). Launched January 3, 1959. Intended as a lunar satellite, it went into orbit around the sun ("artificial planet"), and was renamed "Mechta" (dream). The first artificial satellite to attain escape velocity.

Pioneer IV (U.S.A.). Launched March 3, 1959. Weight 13.4 pounds. Length: 20 inches. Contains two photoelectric cells to send a signal as the vehicle passes the moon. (No camera included.) During countdown, the last three stages of the launching Juno II rocket were set spinning, in order to stabilize the flight. This spin is slowed, so that the cells can "see" the moon. Two five-foot wires with weights at their ends are wrapped around the nose cone; after ten hours of flight, they fly out to their full length and are released. Geiger counters are included in the payload, to detect the existence of a radiation belt around the moon similar to the one around the earth. Pioneer IV passed within 37,000 miles of the lunar surface, 41 hours after launching. It was expected to be in orbit around the sun by March 17, 1959. It continued to send data on radiation levels in outer space when it passed the moon. Estimated perihelion: 91,744 miles; aphelion: 105,829,000 miles. Expected stay in orbit: practically infinite.

—fixed satellite. An artificial satellite revolving around the earth at a distance of 26,000 miles from its center, in an equatorial orbit. Such a satellite would take 24 hours to make one revolution and thus always occupy a fixed position over a point on the earth's equator. Three of these satellites could relay radio, television, and teletype messages continuously, and provide navigational aid. It is planned by NASA to put some in orbit in 1960 or 1961.

—meteorological satellite. Artificial satellite designed for weather observations.

—nomenclature of artificial satellites. A suggestion of the Smithsonian Astrophysical Observatory, with IGY approval, that the nomenclature of artificial satellites be analogous to that now used for newly discovered comets. First, a numeral gives the year of launching and sighting. Next, a Greek letter indicates the order of the satellite within the group of all the satellites launched that year. If a particular stage is to be separately indicated, the Greek letter is followed by an Arabic numeral indicating the brightness of the stage compared to the other; the brightest being indicated by 1, and so on. Thus "1958 γ 2" would indicate the second brightest stage of the third satellite launched in 1958. Similarly, "1958 β" would indicate the second satellite launched in 1958.

—reconnaissance satellite. An artificial satellite used to obtain strategic information through photography, television, etc.

—satelloid. An artificial satellite kept in its orbit by low-thrust motors.

Saturn. Sixth planet of the solar system.

scoring package. *See* RECOVERY PACKAGE.

Scout. Proposed NASA four-stage rocket for launching either satellites or space probes. Named the "poor man's rocket" owing to its relatively low cost: $500,000, as compared with military ballistic missiles which cost $1,000,000. Capable of putting a 150-pound satellite into an orbit at 300 miles altitude or sending a 100-pound instrumentation package to an altitude of some 5000 miles. Used with guidance and spin stabilization. Second stage: an improved Sergeant. Third stage: a scaled-up Vanguard third stage. Solid propellant. Length: 70 feet. Weight: 35,000 pounds.

screaming. RESONANT BURNING. *Colloq.*

scrub. The act of canceling or backing out of a COUNT-DOWN or LAUNCHING sequence because of a breakdown or delay. *Colloq.*

secondary rocket. Landing rocket. (*See under* ROCKET.)

seeker. A homing missile. (*See under* MISSILE.)

semi-active homing. *See under* HOMING.

separation velocity. The velocity of a missile or vehicle when some part is separated from it.

Sergeant. Army surface-to-surface medium-range missile. Inertial guidance, using solid-propellant rocket. Launched in a nearly vertical position from an erector launcher. Will replace the CORPORAL.

shock wave.   A pressure wave set up by the passage of a missile or aircraft at a speed greater than the velocity of sound in the media (Mach 1).

Shrike.   Surface-to-air liquid-propellant rocket missile.

Sidewinder.   Navy air-to-air guided missile. Infrared homing. Solid propellant. High-explosive warhead. Range: 6-7 miles. Speed: Mach 2.5. Length: 9.5 feet. Diameter: 0.42 foot.

SINS.   Shipboard inertial navigation system.

skip-glide bomber.   Type of BOOST-GLIDE bomber that follows an undulating trajectory, glancing or skipping off the upper regions of the atmosphere over long-range flights.

sled, rocket.   *See* ROCKET SLED.

sliver loss.   The portion of a solid PROPELLANT which is inadvertently unburned (typically, 3 to 4 percent).

SM.   Strategic missile.   (*See under* MISSILE.)

SM-62.   Air Force designation for SNARK.

SM-64.   Air Force designation for NAVAHO.

SM-65.   Air Force designation for ATLAS.

SM-68.   Air Force designation for TITAN.

SM-73.   Air Force designation for GOOSE.

SM-75.   Air Force designation for THOR.

Snap III.   System of Nuclear Auxiliary Power III. An atomic battery for use in satellites, consisting of one-hundredth of an ounce of radioactive polonium 210 encased in a molybdenum capsule. Radiation from the polonium heats the capsule to above 700 degrees Fahrenheit. This heat operates thermocouples which generate electric current. Snap III weighs only 5 pounds, and generates 11,500 watt-hours in 130 days. It is estimated that it could keep a satellite's radio and other instruments in operation more than ten times longer than could a chemical battery.

Snark.   Air Force surface-to-surface intercontinental guided missile. Stellar inertial guidance. Powered during cruise by a J-57 turbojet engine. Two zero-length solid-propellant jato boosters. (Also designated SM-62.)

solar generator.   An electric generator powered by radiation from the sun. Used in some artificial satellites.

solar system.   So far as known, the solar system consists of the sun, **9** major planets, 31 satellites, about 1200 minor planets or asteroids, comets, and meteors.

solid fuel.   1. That portion of a solid PROPELLANT exclusive of the oxidizer.
   2. Loosely used for "solid propellant."

solid propellant.   *See* PROPELLANT.

sonance.   The self-excited oscillation of a rocket's gas flow combustion system. A factor in rocket combustion instability. Also called "dynamic instability."

sounding rocket.   *See under* ROCKET.

space bends.   Aeroembolism. *Colloq.*

space cabin.   The portion of a space ship which will contain the passenger(s). It will probably be pressurized, air-conditioned, and temperature-controlled, thus enabling personnel to dispense with their PRESSURE SUITS except for excursions outside the ship. As the early space flights will be mostly ballistic, *i.e.* in FREE FALL, special arrangements will be needed to restrain the movement of objects around the cabin. Other arrangements (air renewal, food, disposal of wastes, etc.) are discussed in current space-flight literature.

space capsule.   Space vehicle, possibly manned, provided with equipment for making a successful re-entry into the earth's atmosphere. (*See* figure 35.) Examples of such equipment:
   1. Heat shield.
   2. Pitch, yaw, and roll jets.
   3. Retrorockets.
   4. A packed parachute (released and used for drag when velocity has been sufficiently reduced.
   5. Inflatable landing bag to cushion the impact in a landing on the ground or act as a float in a landing on the water. (*See* figure 30.)

space flight.   The navigation of interplanetary space by means of a space ship, which may conceivably be achieved by one of the following modes of travel:
   1. Follow a ballistic path, as determined by the gravitational fields of the earth, the planet to which the ship is traveling, and the sun. The space ship is initially set on this path by rocket power which may also be used to brake it at the journey's end.
   2. Use rocket power throughout the journey. The path is not ballistic, but is determined by rocket thrust, plus the aforesaid gravitational fields.
   3. Use a PHOTON SAIL.

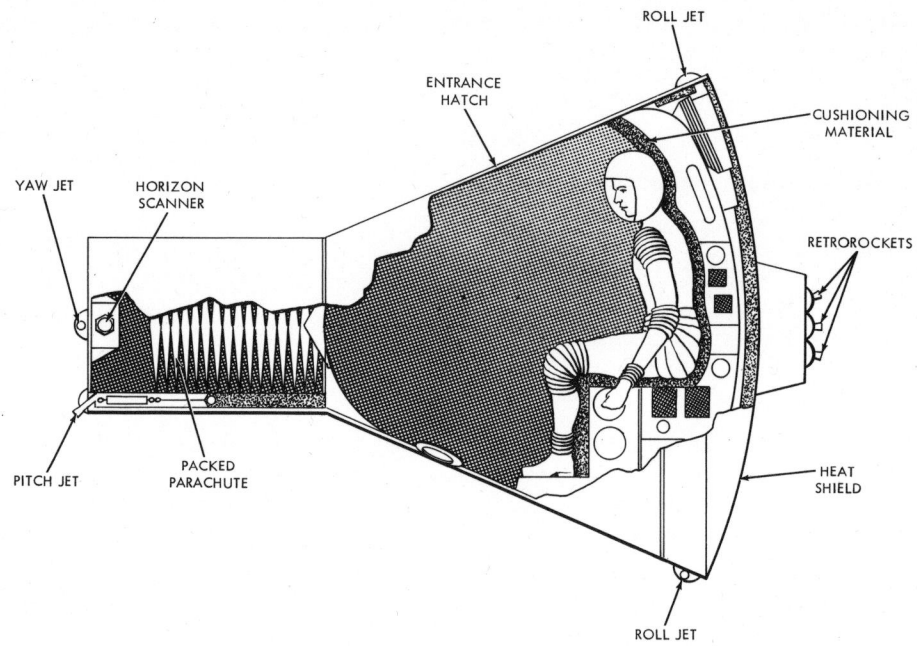

Fig. 35.   Project Mercury Manned Satellite Capsule (NASA)

4. Use artificial gravitational fields (ELECTRO-GRAVITICS).

5. Use space magnetic fields.

Mode 3 is not seriously considered, because of the small accelerations thereby obtained and the limitations on the direction of flight.

Mode 4 lies in the domain of conjecture. If, in some way, an artificial gravitational field could be created, in the direction in which it was desired to propel a space ship, the ship could undergo any required acceleration without damage to the passenger, because the force would act equally on all points of the passenger and ship. (*See* FREE FALL.) Sudden take-off and sudden turns could be made. (It has been suggested that this is how the alleged "flying saucers" are navigated.) The suggestion that we can ever "tame gravity" in such a manner has not met with universal acceptance. Nevertheless, research on this question is rumored to be in progress.

Mode 5 is an even more doubtful category than mode 4. It is proposed that space ships may be propelled and guided by certain magnetic forces alleged to be in space. The existence of such forces has been demonstrated, but not their usability for space flight.

Modes 1 and 2 are in the domain of possibility, especially mode 1. Mode 2 is the more desirable and would be practically ideal for interplanetary (not interstellar) flights because of the high speeds obtainable and the constant gravity-simulating acceleration or deceleration, which would permit normal sensations instead of "WEIGHTLESSNESS" for the passengers. However, mode 2 will not be realizable until atomic fuels of a type as yet unknown are available.

Mode 1 is the only mode being seriously considered today. It may become practicable for unmanned flights at any time, now, but it possesses two grave disadvantages for manned flight: 1) the passengers would be in FREE FALL, *i.e.* weightless, for the greater part of the voyage; 2) coasting speed (until greatly improved fuels have become available) would be only a few miles per second. A trip to the moon would last several days, to Mars, several months. Whereas, using mode 2, a trip to the moon could take 3½ hours,

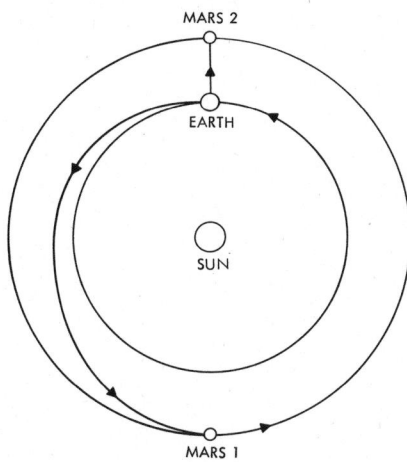

FIG. 36. Paths to Mars: 1) For Vehicle Using Conventional Fuel: 2) For Vehicle Using Fuel of the Future (Rockets, Missiles, and Space Travel, by Willy Ley. (The Viking Press, Inc.))

and a trip to Mars, two days (assuming an acceleration of 1 *g* for the first half of the journey and a deceleration of 1 *g* for the second half).

Figure 36 shows the probable paths of a trip to Mars using modes 1 and 2, respectively. The earth is shown in its position at the beginning of the flight. "Mars 1" and "Mars 2" are the positions of Mars at the end of flights by modes 1 and 2, respectively. The "Mars 1" path, a TANGENTIAL ELLIPSE, is the most economic path.

When mode 2 becomes practicable, interplanetary flight will be quick and comfortable. Interstellar flight, however, will still be remote, because the nearest star is four light-years away and it has not been considered possible, since the acceptance of the Theory of Relativity, that matter can move at more than the velocity of light.

One of the more daring speculations is that voyages to distant stars may be undertaken using the method of "time dilatation." A voyage actually taking 100 years could be compressed into a few months. Cruising velocity would have to be very close indeed to the velocity of light and, since a corresponding increase in mass would then take place, the use of rockets would necessitate an enormously high mass ratio. If space flight mode 4 ever becomes realizable, flights using time dilatation might also become possible.

space law. A proposed code of international law currently under study that would govern the use or control of space by different nations. Operation and enforcement of this code would be similar to that for maritime law. It has been suggested that air law should end and space law begin at the altitude where sustained flight by aircraft becomes impossible, *i.e.* about 55 miles above the earth.

spaceman. ASTRONAUT. *Colloq.*

space medicine. A branch of medicine dealing with the special physiological and psychological conditions that will affect passengers in a space ship. These include: weightlessness, lack of exercise, high accelerations, atmospheric composition, food restrictions, boredom, possible blindness due to sudden flashes of sunlight, ebullism, etc.

space probe. An exploratory excursion into space for data-gathering purposes.

space ship. A passenger and/or cargo-carrying craft designed for the navigation of interplanetary (and, eventually, interstellar) space. (*See also* SPACE FLIGHT.)

space station. A proposed large manned artificial satellite that can remain in orbit a considerable length of time. May be rotated to simulate gravity. (*See* ARTIFICIAL GRAVITY.) Will carry instruments for making observations similar to those made by smaller satellites, but on a more extensive scale; also, probably, a telescope. Astronomical observations made from a space station will reveal a wealth of detail unseen by any telescope on the earth, because of the absence of atmosphere.

Space stations may also be used as stopping places for space ships in interplanetary flight. Passengers will change from the streamlined vehicle in which they left the earth into a roomier, more commodious vehicle which need not be streamlined since it will be used only in outer space. Takeoff from the station, that is to say, attaining escape velocity, will be easier than from the earth because the station will already have orbital velocity.

Figure 37 shows a model space station proposed by Werner von Braun.

space suit. *See* PRESSURE SUIT.

FIG. 37. Space Station As Conceived By von Braun   (Die Eroerung des Mondes, by Werner von Braun, illustrated by Chesley Bonestell, Fred Freeman, and Rolf Klap (S. Fischer Verlag, 1954.))

space taxi. Vehicle for transferring passengers from a ferry rocket to a space station, or from the station to a space ship. *Colloq.*

space vehicle. Any vehicle capable of transporting a payload outside of the earth's atmosphere during all or a portion of its flight. At present, rockets provide the only practical means for propulsion of a space vehicle. (*See also* SPACE FLIGHT.)

Spaerobee. NRL rocket designed to investigate the arctic ionosphere, especially with regard to "polar radio blackout." Expected to reach altitudes of 270 miles and over.

Sparrow. A class of Navy air-to-air guided missiles. Sparrow III uses radar homing, and is directed in the first seconds of flight by launching aircraft. Warhead is 50 percent more powerful than previous air-to-air missiles. Operational. Can attack targets at high and low altitudes. Speed: over 1000 mph attained immediately after launching. Length: 12 feet. Diameter: 8 inches. Weight: 350 pounds.

specific impulse. *See* IMPULSE, SPECIFIC.

Sputnik. Class of USSR artificial satellites. Sputnik I was first earth satellite to be placed in orbit. (*See under* SATELLITE, ARTIFICIAL.) "Sputnik" is Russian word for "space traveler."

squib. A positive-acting, one-shot explosive switch. The contacts are brought together or separated by the action of an electrically activated, shaped, explosive charge.

SS-10, SS-11. French-designed anti-tank guided missiles. The SS-10 was tested and evaluated by the U.S. Army and is being procured as a replacement for the DART.

SSM. Surface-to-surface missile.

stability, dynamic. The characteristic motion of a missile returning to its steady-state condition after a disturbance has produced an unbalanced motion.

stability, inherent. Missile characteristic causing it, when disturbed, to return to its normal attitude of flight without the use of a control system.

stages, rocket. See ROCKET, MULTI-STAGE.

staging. The jettisoning, at some desired flight point, of certain missile components that are no longer needed.

star-tracking guidance. CELESTIAL-NAVIGATION GUIDANCE.

static firing. Ground test of a rocket engine; captive firing.

static testing. Ground test of a missile or vehicle, simulating flight conditions; captive test.

stay time. In liquid propellants, the average time spent by each gas molecule or atom within the combustion chamber.

stellerator. An apparatus currently in use at Project Matterhorn to produce PLASMA PINCH. It consists of an evacuated tube into which low-pressure deuterium is injected and confined in a MAGNETIC BOTTLE by the magnetic confining field. Two models have been described. In one, the tube has the shape of the figure eight in order to overcome the effect of the diminishing magnetic-field gradient in the dissipating plasma stream. In the other model ("racetrack"), the shape is oval; the same result is obtained by using secondary helical magnetic field windings.

step rocket. MULTI-STAGE ROCKET. (*See under* ROCKET.)

STOL. Short take-off and landing.

strategic missile. *See under* Missile.

Strategic Missile Squadron. The smallest Air Force strategic missile organization having administrative capability. It consists of from three to six flights, with appropriate command and administrative elements.

Strategic Missile Support Squadron. An Air Force organization assigned to the support base, providing support for all missile units at the launch base.

Strategic Missile Wing. An Air Force organization consisting of one strategic missile support squadron and two or more strategic missile squadrons.

Stratoscope. *See* Project Stratoscope.

stratosphere. This term was formerly used to designate all space above the tropopause, *i.e.* above about 10 miles altitude. It is now more often used to designate the layer of the atmosphere between the tropopause and about 16 miles up, where the mesosphere is said to begin. All but the highest portions of the stratosphere are suitable for jet-plane flight, but less so for rocket flight.

STS. Ship-to-shore.

SUBROC. Navy missile. Fired underwater from conventional torpedo tube, but most of its course is through the air. Possibly carries nuclear warhead. Range: 25 to 50 miles.

SUM. Surface-to-underwater missile.

sun satellite. Artificial satellite orbiting the sun.

Sunseeker. Photoelectric device in a rocket nose cone, satellite, or space vehicle, causing an instrument to be oriented toward the sun at all times.

supersonic. Faster than sound. *See also* Mach number.

synergy curve. The most advantageous path from launch to burnout that a rocket can pursue in order to get a satellite in orbit. (The term "advantageous" is used in the sense of transferring as much of the energy as possible to the rocket and as little as possible to the exhaust.)

T

T-1. USSR surface-to-surface guided rocket missile. Similar to the German V-2, but with a greatly increased range. Radio-inertial guidance. Liquid oxygen and alcohol propellant. Range: 400-600 miles. (Also designated M-101.)

T-2. USSR surface-to-surface two-stage guided rocket missile. Radio-inertial guidance up to burnout. Liquid oxygen and alcohol propellant. Range: 1800 miles. A continuation of the T-1 program. (Also designated M-103.)

T-3. USSR surface-to-surface two-stage guided rocket missile. Radio-inertial guidance. Oxygen/kerosene propellant. Range: 5000 miles. (Also designated M-104.)

T-3A. USSR surface-to-surface two-stage guided rocket missile. Follow-on to the T-3 with increased range (6200 miles) but less payload capability.

T-4. USSR two-stage IRBM. Radio-inertial guidance. Carries an 1800-pound atomic warhead. Oxygen/hydrazine propellant. Range: 1000 miles. (Also designated M-102.)

T-4A. USSR surface-to-surface boost-glide missile. Carries a 3100-pound atomic warhead. Range: 12,000 miles. May be manned.

T-5. USSR surface-to-surface three-stage ballistic missile. A copy of the German Rheinbote. Nitric acid/hydrazine booster propellant. Range: 100 miles.

T-5B. USSR surface-to-surface ballistic rocket missile. Carried on a self-propelled launcher. Range: 25 miles.

T-5C. USSR surface-to-surface rocket missile. A smaller version of T-5B. Solid propellant. Range: 15-20 miles.

T-6. USSR surface-to-air two-stage guided missile. Similar to NIKE class. Radar guidance. Solid propellant. Operational ceiling: 60,000 feet. The high-explosive warhead carries a proximity fuze.

T-7. USSR surface-to-air high-altitude guided missile. Inertial guidance. Liquid oxygen and hydrazine propellant. Peak altitude: 60 miles.

T-7A. USSR surface-to-surface guided missile. Radio-inertial guidance. Superseding T-5 owing to greater accuracy. Liquid oxygen and hydrogen propellant. Uses mobile launching equipment. Range: 100 miles.

T-8. USSR surface-to-air guided missile. Infrared guidance. Initial acceleration given by solid-propellant boosters. Nitric acid/alcohol propellant. Range: 15 miles.

tactical missile. *See under* MISSILE.

take-off. The instant at which a missile leaves the launching pad in flight.

take-off weight. The weight of a missile at take-off. In rockets, take-off weight greatly exceeds weight at BURNOUT.

Talos.   Navy surface-to-air hypersonic guided missile. Guidance is in two stages: beam-riding and then passive homing. Boosted by a solid-propellant rocket, then flies by ramjet. Range: 70 miles (approximately). (Also designated IM-70.)

tactical missile.   *See under* MISSILE.

tandem missile.   *See under* MISSILE.

tangential ellipse.   Most economical space flight transfer ellipse from the orbit of one planet to that of another. Grazes both orbits. Also known as "Hohmann orbit." (*See* figure 36).

Tartar.   Navy surface-to-air hypersonic guided missile. Similar to TERRIER but smaller, using a booster. Beam guidance. Speed: in excess of Mach 2.

TCBM.   TRANSCONTINENTAL BALLISTIC MISSILE.

telemetry.   The branch of communications concerned with the obtaining, processing, and transmitting of data over large distances. For space vehicles, this involves the obtaining of data by instruments, computers, etc., and transmitting it by coded radio. This generally involves a multiplexing system capable of handling a number of data transducers.

Terrier.   Navy class of surface-to-air hypersonic guided missiles. Beam guidance. Uses a solid-propellant booster. Speed: Mach 2.5 (maximum). Terrior I range: 10 miles. Terrier II range: 20 miles.

test vehicle.   A missile launched for test purposes.

theodolite, intermediate range alignment.   Instrument used in U.S.A. to align the JUPITER IRBM prior to launching. Uses optical, electronic, and mechanical system to measure degree of misalignment of missile axes and to drive it automatically to correct alignment.

thermal barrier.   The velocity range in which metals are subjected to dangerously high temperatures due to atmospheric friction, *viz.* 2000 mph and over. The problems of the thermal barrier must be met by designing aircraft that will withstand temperatures above 2500 degrees Fahrenheit.

thermojet.   *See* JET.

thermonuclear.   Pertaining to nuclear processes caused by heat, especially to NUCLEAR FUSION caused by heat of a fission bomb explosion. *See* ATOMIC ENERGY.

thermonuclear engine.   A rocket engine powered by NUCLEAR FUSION, possibly attainable when controlled fusion has become a reality. (*See also* ION ROCKET and PLASMA PINCH.)

thermosphere. The layer of the atmosphere between 40 and 300 miles altitude above the surface of the earth, so named because of the temperature variation within it. Temperatures range from a minimum at 40 miles altitude to several thousand degrees at 250 miles. (Note that at 250 miles the atmosphere is so rarefied that its "temperature" is a purely statistical quantity. It would not appreciably raise the temperature of a body traveling through it at moderate velocity.) The thermosphere is roughly coextensive with the IONOSPHERE.

Thor. Air Force surface-to-surface IRBM. Inertial guidance during the powered first portion of the flight. Liquid oxygen and kerosene propellant. Thrust: 165,000 pounds. Range: 1500-2200 miles. Speed: 10,000 mph (maximum). (Also designated SM-75.)

thrust. Force exercised on the body of a rocket by the expulsion of combustion products through the exhaust nozzle. This force acts along the axis of thrust.

—*static thrust.* The thrust produced by a jet, rocket, or propeller engine when held stationary.

thrust axis. Instantaneous direction of rocket thrust.

thrust specific fuel consumption. A figure of merit for jet engines: the ratio of pounds of fuel consumed per second to pounds of thrust. (*See also* SPECIFIC IMPULSE.)

thrust spoiler. A system of shutters over the end of a jet exhaust pipe to destroy most of the thrust at idling speeds and thus reduce the landing thrust. Not in general use.

thrust termination equipment. A component of a missile propulsion system used to terminate thrust at a predetermined time to achieve proper positioning of the point of impact of the missile or payload.

thrust vector control. A means of controlling the attitude and path of a missile by jet deflection, operated by signals from the autopilot.

Thunderbird. British surface-to-air guided missile. Sustainer motor, four solid-propellant rocket boosters. Slant range: 24 miles. Operational ceiling: over 60,000 feet.

T-hung-lian-keng-mu. Title of a 13th-century Chinese chronicle, the earliest-known document to mention the use of rockets as missiles, *viz.* against the Mongols at the siege of Kai-fung-fu (Pien-king) in 1232 A.D.

time dilatation. The slowing down or "stretching" of time intervals between systems traveling at different velocities, a phenomenon predicted by

Einstein in his Special Theory of Relativity. If a system B, is traveling with a velocity V relative to another system A, then a time interval measured as t_A by a clock in System A will be measured as t_B in System B, so that

$$t_B = t_A \sqrt{1 - \frac{V^2}{c^2}} \tag{1}$$

where c = velocity of light.

(This time dilatation is related to a corresponding contraction of length in the direction of motion:

$$l_B = l_A \sqrt{1 - \frac{V^2}{c^2}}.$$

This hypothesis was put forward by Fitzgerald and Lorentz, prior to Einstein, to explain the negative result of the Michelson-Morley ether-drift experiment.)

If V is very close to c, t_B will be much less than t_A. It has been stated that this principle might be utilized in space flight over interstellar distances. If a space ship were traveling, say, at 99.5% of the VELOCITY OF LIGHT, its clock would indicate the passage of time at one-tenth the rate of an earth clock:

$$t_B = t_A \sqrt{1 - (0.995)^2} = 0.1 \, t_A \tag{2}$$

Thus a trip requiring 4 years of time measured in System A would require only .4 years or 4.8 months in System B. It would thus become a 5-month trip to the passengers, for all biological processes would also slow up with the clock.

With a 99.995% ship-to-light velocity ratio, a 1:100 time ratio could be obtained. The passengers would be able to travel to distant stars in what would be to them only a year (though, on their return, all their friends would probably be dead).

It is not supposed that such velocities can be obtained with present-day techniques. Even when new, dreamed-of atomic fuels become available, and EXHAUST VELOCITIES of the order of one-tenth the velocity of light realizable, the higher velocity ratio required would necessitate an exceedingly high MASS RATIO. The mass ratio would be still further increased by the fact that a corresponding "mass dilatation" would take place. A mass M_o traveling at velocity V, is increased to mass M, where:

$$M = \frac{M_o}{\sqrt{1 - \frac{V^2}{c^2}}} \tag{3}$$

Time dilatation and rockets do not go well together. Possibly if the dreamed-of "taming of gravity" ever becomes a reality, it may be used in conjunction with time dilatation. (*See* mode 4 under SPACE FLIGHT.)

Early in the history of relativity, the objection was raised that time dilatation as expressed in equation 1 makes an unwarrantable distincition between the moving system and the system at rest. If System B is moving with respect to System A, then System A is likewise moving with respect to System B. From the point of view of an observer situated in System B, it is system A that is moving. Therefore, it would seem that it is just as true to say:

$$t_A = t_B \sqrt{1 - \frac{V^2}{c^2}}, \tag{4}$$

which is in disagreement with equation 1.

(Note that since velocity is squared in equations 1 and 3, its direction is immaterial. When System B is considered to be the traveler, the conditions prevailing during its outward journey are the same as those prevailing during its inward journey, not reverse conditions. Likewise the fact that System A's motion relative to System B is the reverse of System B's motion relative to System A does not affect the problem.)

This difficulty is known as the "Clock Paradox," or "Twin Paradox," and may be resolved by invoking the General Theory of Relativity. The paradox arises from the assumption that the problem is a symmetrical one, *i.e.* that Systems A and B are precisely similar. This is not so, except during the time interval when their relative velocity is constant. In order to achieve this velocity, System B is subjected to new forces and thereby new accelerations and decelerations with respect to the rest of the universe; System A is not. Although these accelerations may be very short in duration compared to the period of constant velocities, it may be shown by application of the General Theory of Relativity that they are of paramount importance. If we assume that System B is at rest and System A is set in motion then we must also assume that the whole universe is subjected to new accelerations and decelerations, along with System A. This, according to the general theory, would set up gravitational fields, which would alter the rate of the System A clock in the reverse sense of that alteration predicted by the special theory.

A brief sketch of the outlines of this analysis must suffice for this publication. It is first assumed that System B travels and System A is at rest, as originally stated. System B is subjected to forces; System A is not. This leads in the expected manner to equation 1, though by a more complicated mathematical route than with the use of the special theory alone.

Next, it is assumed that System B is at rest, while System A travels. But the assumptions must be in accordance with the facts. System B is still subjected to the original forces, but is kept at rest by the counteraction of superimposed gravitational fields (called into being by the supposed acceleration and deceleration of the rest of the universe). These gravitational fields "accelerate" and "decelerate" System A. As a result, when System A is "moving at constant velocity" (and is therefore far from System B), its gravitational scalar potential is increased. This, as demonstrated by the general theory, *increases* the speed of the System A clock as observed in System B. Finally, equation 1 is reached—not equation 4. Thus, the slow-down of the System B clock as compared with the System A clock occurs regardless of the observer's point of view—provided that it is System B which is accelerated and decelerated with respect to the rest of the universe.

To summarize:—By extending the proof of time ·dilatation to embrace the general as well as the special theory of relativity, the conclusion is reached that a traveler who leaves the earth on a space voyage, and returns, will, on comparing his clock (counting days, weeks, etc.) with that of a man who has stayed at home, find that his clock records the lesser time elapsed. And the man who stayed at home will agree.

A program has been scheduled, under NASA auspices, to prove or disprove the existence of time dilatation experimentally by observing the count of satellite-borne atomic clocks. Changes in clock period due to velocity and changed gravitational potential will be measured.

Titan.   Air Force surface-to-surface two-stage ICBM. Inertial/radio-inertial guidance during the powered first portion of the flight. Liquid oxygen and JP-6 propellant. Unlike ATLAS, the second stage is not fired until the first stage has completed its course. Thrust: 300,000 pounds. Range: 5500 miles. Speed: 15,000 mph (maximum). (Also designated SM-68.)

TM.   Tactical missile. (*See under* MISSILE.)

TM-61.   Air Force designation for MATADOR.

TM-76.   Air Force designation for MACE.

topping.   Replacing propellants lost through vaporization and initial consumption from the ground supply.

total impulse.   *See* IMPULSE, TOTAL.

tracker.   A device operating on optical, radar, infrared, or other detecting principle that follows the movement of a missile in flight and provides this data in some usable form.

traffic-handling capacity.   The ability of a missile system to control multiple missiles against one or more targets.

trajectory.   The path of any missile (jet, rocket, etc.) or projectile (bullet, shell, etc.).

transcontinental ballistic missile. A future, advanced form of ICBM, capable of 12,500-mile ranges, *i.e.* capable of being fired to any point on the earth's surface.

trim. A steady-state or aircraft condition wherein the control surfaces on a missile are deflected to provide the necessary lifting force, such that the sum of the moments acting on the missile are zero.

tropopause. *See* TROPOSPHERE.

troposphere. The layer of the atmosphere between ground and about 10 miles altitude above the earth. Here, temperature generally decreases with altitude, clouds form, and convection is active. The upper limit of the troposphere is called the "tropopause."

tumble. Of an oblong satellite. To rotate about its shorter axis, end-over-end. It is the tumbling action that produces the twinkling effect when the satellite is viewed at dawn or dusk.

turbo-compound. A combination of TURBOPROP with a conventional reciprocating engine. The engine's exhaust gases drive the turbine which, in turn, drives the propeller and feeds back to the engine crankshaft.

turbofan. An advanced form of TURBOJET with greater propulsive efficiency, higher take-off thrust and lower noise level.

turbojet. A type of aircraft or missile which, like the RAMJET, derives its velocity from the intake of air at the forward end, combustion of fuel, and ejection of combustion products at the rear end. Unlike the ramjet, it has rotating parts. The expanding combustion products drive a turbine situated between the combustion chamber and exhaust nozzle. The turbine drives a rotary compressor situated between the combustion chamber and the intake nozzle.

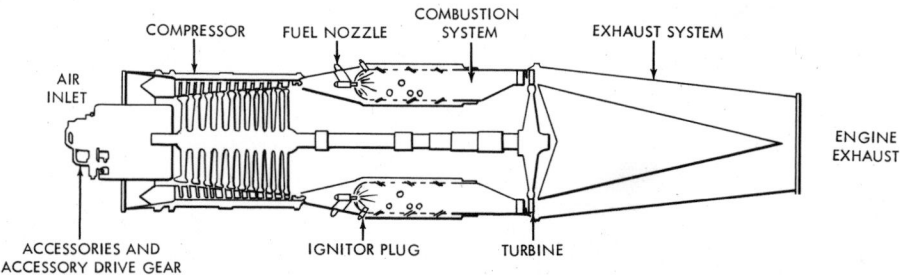

FIG. 38.   Turbojet   (General Electric Company)

turboprop. A type of aircraft or missile similar to the TURBOJET but having, as an additional feature, a propeller in the front of the gas intake.

This propeller is driven by the turbine through reduction gearing. The turbine drives the compressor at its own rotation rate. More of the energy in the combustion gases is used to drive the turbine than in the turbojet. The jet is of lower velocity. Figure 39 shows a turboprop with regeneration and a tandem compound turboprop.

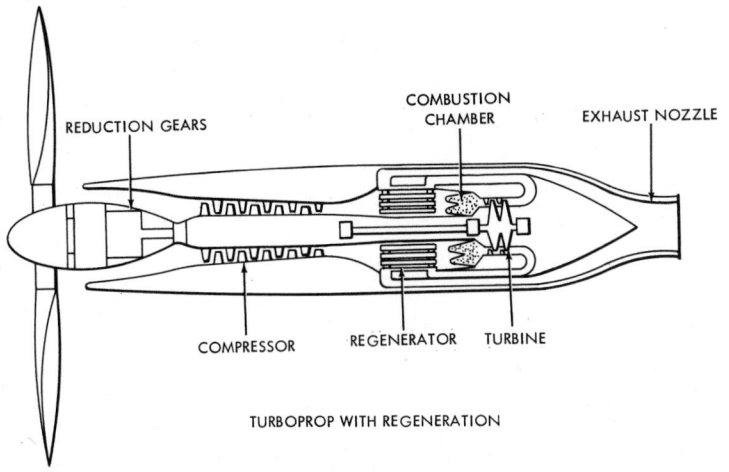

TURBOPROP WITH REGENERATION

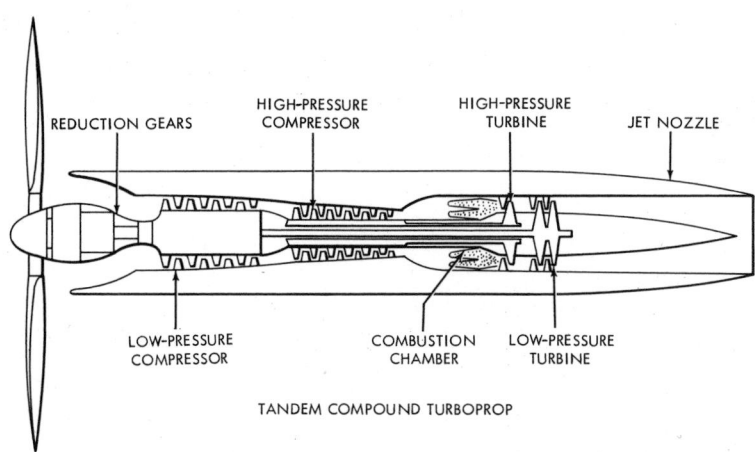

TANDEM COMPOUND TURBOPROP

FIG. 39. Turboprops (Westinghouse Electric Corporation)

turboramjet. A TURBOJET having, as an additional feature, a second combustion chamber between the turbine and the exhaust nozzle. Additional fuel is injected into this chamber.

turborocket. A hybrid of TURBOJET and ROCKET ENGINE. The rocket engines take the place of the jet combustion chamber; their exhaust drives the turbine that drives the rotary compressor. Air received at the intake nozzle and compressed by the compressor mixes with the rocket exhaust gases. This provides the major part of the combustion. Additional fuel may be injected at this point.

U

UAM. Underwater-to-air missile.

UFO. Unidentified flying object. (*See* FLYING SAUCER.)

ullage. The volume of a propellant tank in excess of propellant volume. Provided to allow for thermal expansion of the propellant and for evolved gaseous products.

umbilical boom. A support for an UMBILICAL CABLE.

umbilical cable. A servicing and test connection to a missile that provides electrical and/or pneumatic access to the missile before it is fired. The umbilical cable is disconnected just prior to, or at, firing.

umbilical connector. The connector that terminates an UMBILICAL CABLE and mates with the umbilical connector receptacle. The connector is usually of a quick-disconnect or breakaway type.

Uranus. Seventh planet of the solar system. The first to be "discovered," since the planets closer to the earth are readily seen.

USM. Underwater-to-surface missile.

V

V-1. Early pulse-jet missile used against the United Kingdom by the Germans toward the end of World War II, prior to the use of the V-2. The V-1 was called the "buzz bomb" in reference to the noise made by its pulse valve. It was not designed to hit a specific point but, rather, to come down over U.K. territory and detonate when its jet motor ceased to function. Altitude: 2000-3000 feet. Range: 150 miles. Speed: about 360 mph. (Also designated FZG-76.)

V-2. The first long-range rocket with a mission, an early prototype of the IRBM. Used by the Germans against England toward the end of World War II, following the use of the V-1. Several were successfully fired over London. Designed in the research institute at Peenemunde. Propellant: alcohol and liquid oxygen. Thrust: 60,000 pounds. Maximum speed: 1 mile/second. Maximum range: 199 miles. Length: 46 feet. Diameter over fins: 11 feet 8 inches. (Also designated A-4.)

Van Allen layer. The RADIATION BELT recently discovered by means of Explorer I and probed by Pioneer III.

Vanguard. **1.** A class of artificial satellites. *See* OPERATION VANGUARD and SATELLITE, ARTIFICIAL.

2. Navy surface-to-air LAUNCH VEHICLE. A three-stage rocket used to orbit the VANGUARD SATELLITE. First stage: liquid propellant, 30,000 pounds thrust, 4000 mph velocity at burnout at 36 miles altitude. Second stage: liquid propellant, 11,000 mph velocity at burnout at 130 miles altitude. Vehicle coasts up to 300 miles altitude where second stage separates from third. Third stage: solid propellant, 18,000 mph velocity at burnout. Overall length: 72 feet. Weight: 22,000 pounds.

Vega. One of a new, proposed class of rockets designed to put a 370-pound payload on the moon, carry instruments to Mars or Venus, or put a 7400-pound satellite into a 300-mile orbit. Will use an ATLAS-type first stage, VANGUARD second stage. The third stage will be a new rocket, carrying a fuel which will be ignited in outer space.

vehicle, space. *See* SPACE VEHICLE.

velocity, escape. *See* ESCAPE VELOCITY.

velocity, exhaust. *See* EXHAUST VELOCITY.

velocity, orbital. *See* ORBITAL VELOCITY.

velocity ratio. The ratio of the velocity of a rocket at BURNOUT to the velocity (with respect to the rocket) of exhaust. Velocity ratio for a single-stage rocket is related to *mass ratio* (ratio of mass at launching to mass at burnout) by the equation:

$$\text{Velocity ratio} = \log_e (\text{mass ratio}).$$

Venus. Second planet of the solar system.

Veronique. French high-altitude research rocket.

Viking. A high-altitude research rocket. (Also designated "Marco Polo" and "Neptune.")

VTOL. Vertical take-off and landing.

W

WAC Corporal. A high-altitude research rocket later developed into the AEROBEE. Contains solid propellant booster and liquid propellant motor.

Wagtail. Air Force air-to-ground missile. Uses retrorockets after launch to achieve a very low velocity before ignition of the solid-propellant engine.

Can be launched from a low-flying bomber and climb over obstacles such as hills.

warhead. The explosive portion of a missile.

warhead yield. The weight of TNT having the same energy release as a given nuclear warhead.

weapon system. Air Force designation for the combination of a missile or other military device plus all the ground support and ancillary equipment required to use the weapon.

weather eye. Meteorological satellite. *Colloq.*

weightlessness. *See* Free fall.

window. Strips of metal dropped or expelled from missiles or aircraft to create echoes for confusion purposes against radar or guided missiles. May be attached to small parachutes. Also called "rope."

wind tunnel. A device for testing aircraft and missiles. The equipment to be tested is placed in the tunnel and subjected to strong currents of wind, simulating speed, and high temperatures. Aerodynamic characteristics, heat transfer, and attitude control can be measured. Figure 40 shows a wind tunnel used in testing the Polaris ballistic missile. It produces speeds up to 15,000 mph and temperatures 6000 degrees hotter than the sun's surface. Gas in the arc chamber heats instantly to 18,000 degrees Fahrenheit, explodes through the tunnel, and blasts against the missile's nose.

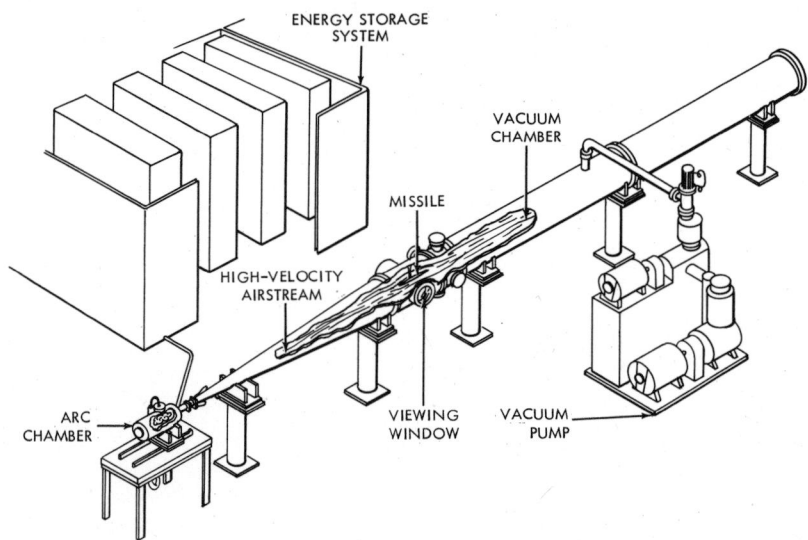

Fig. 40. Wind Tunnel for Polaris Testing (Astronautics, March 1958. (The American Rocket Society))

Wizard.   Air Force ground-to-air missile system.

WS.   WEAPON SYSTEM.

WS-107.   *See* TITAN.

WS-117L.   RECONNAISSANCE SATELLITE.

WS-131B.   Air Force air-to-surface missile.

WS-132.   Air Force air-to-ground missile weapon system for launch from a B-52 aircraft.

WS-138A.   Air Force air-to-ground missile weapon system. May be based on BOLD ORION missile.

X

X.   The prefix "X" is used by the Air Force to designate an experimental vehicle.

X-1.   Air Force liquid-propellant experimental rocket. The first manned vehicle to exceed the speed of sound in level flight. Powered by 6000-pound thrust rocket engine fueled on liquid oxygen and alcohol. Powered flight could be sustained for 2½ minutes.

X-15.   Manned research vehicle with pilot control being developed and tested for the Air Force. The X-15 is expected to provide data on high-altitude (100 miles) high-speed (3600 mph) flight. The vehicle uses aerodynamic control surfaces within the sensible atmosphere and monopropellant rocket thrust beyond the sensible atmosphere. Launched from a B-52 bomber in flight.

X-17.   Three-stage solid-propellant manned rocket used by Air Force to test re-entry vehicles. The rocket is designed to take off vertically to reach an altitude of approximately 200 miles, then tilt earthward and, with motors still firing, re-enter the atmosphere at about Mach 15.

Z

zero-*g*.   Zero-gravity. Another term for weightlessness. (*See also* FREE FALL.)

zero-launch.   *See under* LAUNCH.

zero-length launcher.   *See under* LAUNCHER.

Zuni.   Navy air-to-air and air-to-surface missile. Used in fighter aircraft.

MISSILE DATA

	Atlas	**Bomarc**
Service	Air Force	Air Force
Type	ICBM	Surface-to-air
Guidance	Doppler-radar command	GCC/radar homing
Range (*miles*)	5500-6200	200-250
Velocity	15,000 mph max.	Mach 2.5 max.
Thrust (*lbs*)	300,000	10,000-12,000
Propulsion System	3-stage rocket	2 ramjet engines (rocket boost)
Propellants	Liquid oxygen and kerosene	Booster: JP-4 & WFNA 2nd stage: (liquid)
Weight (*lbs*)	243,000	15,000+

Bullpup	**Comet 1**	**Comet 2**
Navy	USSR	USSR
Air-to-surface	Surface-to-surface	Surface-to-surface
Visual reference radio command	———	Inertial
5 (approx.)	75-100	620
Mach 1-2	3225 mph	5700 mph
	53,250	99,000
———	———	———
———		———
Solid	Solid	Solid
540	20,000	41,500

MISSILE DATA (cont.)

	Corporal	**Dart**
Service	Army	Army
Type	Surface-to-surface	Surface-to-surface
Guidance	Command	Optical
Range (miles)	75 (100 max.)	1.14
Velocity	———	Mach 1
Thrust (lbs)	———	———
Propulsion System	Ballistic rocket	Rocket
Propellants	Nitric acid & aniline	Solid
Weight (lbs)	12,000	100

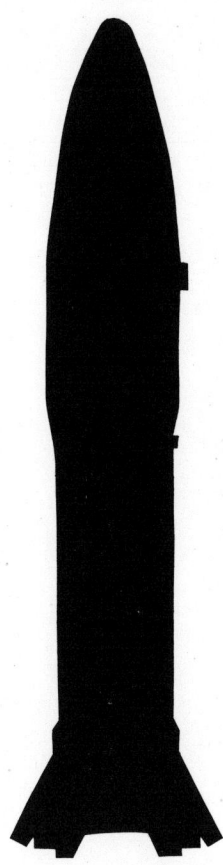

Falcon I	**Falcon II**	**Genie**
Air Force	Air Force	Air Force
Air-to-air	Air-to-air	Air-to-air
Radar homing	Infrared homing	———
5 (approx.)	5 (approx.)	1.5
Mach 2+	Mach 2+	———
6000	6000	———
Rocket	Rocket	Rocket
Solid	Solid	Solid
100	100	———

MISSILE DATA (cont.)

	Golem-1	**Golem-2**
Service	USSR	USSR
Type	Underwater-to-surface	Underwater-to-surface
Guidance	Radio-inertial	Radio-inertial
Range (*miles*)	400	1240
Velocity	5425 mph	9325 mph
Thrust (*lbs*)	121,200	71,500
Propulsion System	Rocket	Rocket
Propellants	Liquid oxygen & alcohol	Nitric acid & alcohol
Weight (*lbs*)	33,125	75,000

Golem-3	**Goose**	**Hawk I**
USSR	Air Force	Army
Underwater-to-air	Surface-to-air	Surface-to-air
Infrared homing	Inertial	Radar homing
7.45	2000+	22 max.
1860 mph	High subsonic	
15,000	5000+	
Rocket	Rocket-boosted turbojet	2-stage rocket
Solid	Booster: solid	Solid
	2nd stage: JP	
4625		1200

MISSILE DATA (cont.)

	Honest John	**J-1**
Service	Army	USSR
Type	Surface-to-surface	Surface-to-surface
Guidance	None	Radio
Range (*miles*)	18-20	370
Velocity	1120 mph	519 mph
Thrust (*lbs*)	———	2000
Propulsion System	Rocket	Rocket-boosted pulse jet
Propellants	Solid	Booster: solid 2nd stage: kerosene
Weight (*lbs*)	6000	2640

J-2	**J-3**	**Jupiter**
USSR	USSR	Army
Anti-submarine	Anti-submarine	IRBM
Radio	Radio or radar	Inertial
525	450	1500-2000
645 mph	875 mph max.	10,000 mph
4850	15,000	150,000-165,000
Rocket-boosted axial-flow turbine	Rocket-boosted ramjet	Rocket
Booster: solid 2nd stage: kerosene	Booster: solid 2nd stage: kerosene	Liquid oxygen & kerosene
16,100	18,700	105,000

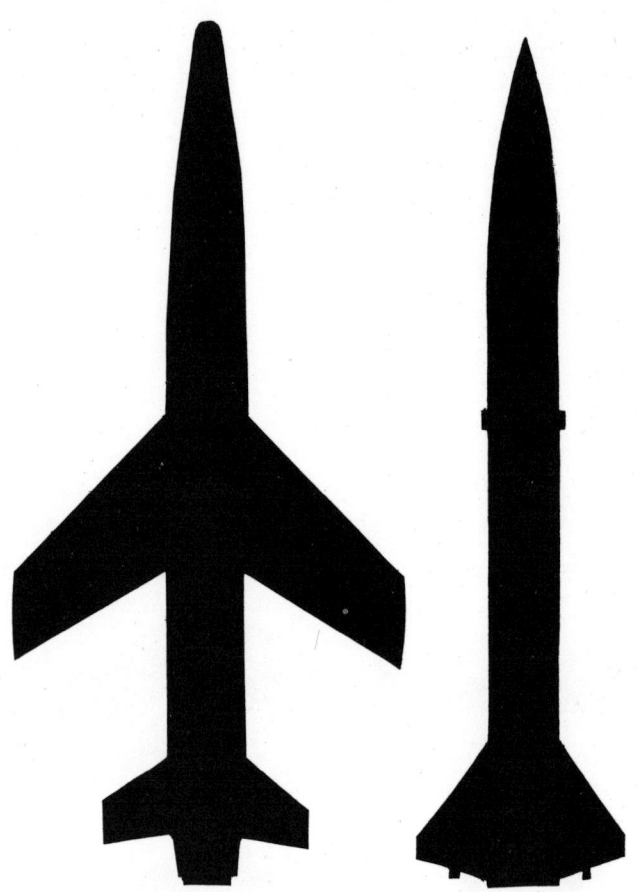

MISSILE DATA (cont.)

	Lacrosse	**Little John**
Service	Army	Army
Type	Surface-to-surface	Surface-to-surface
Guidance	Terminal (by a forward observer)	None
Range (miles)	20	10
Velocity	Mach 2	1860 mph
Thrust (lbs)	———	———
Propulsion System	Rocket	Rocket
Propellants	Solid	Solid
Weight (lbs)	———	980

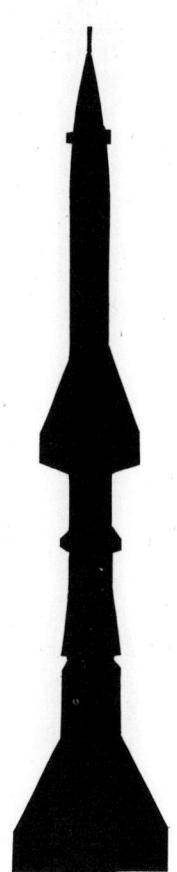  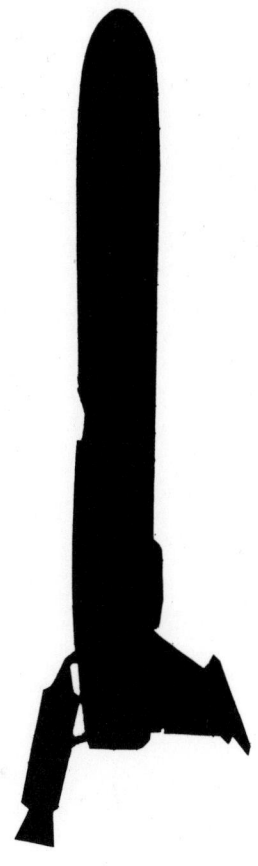

M-2	**M-100A**	**Mace**
USSR	USSR	Air Force
Surface-to-air	Air-to-air	Surface-to-surface
Radar and infrared	Infrared or unguided	ATRAN or inertial
37.25	3.4	700 max.
1550 mph	1740 mph	Mach 0.9 max.
4625	100	5200
Booster (rocket) and sustainer	Rocket	Booster (rocket) & sustainer
Solid	Solid	Booster: solid sustainer: JP
3970	18.5	13,800

MISSILE DATA (cont.)

	Matador	**ME**
Service	Air Force	USSR
Type	Surface-to-surface	Surface-to-surface
Guidance	MSQ/Shanicle	———
Range (miles)	700	———
Velocity	Mach 0.9 max.	535 mph
Thrust (lbs)	Booster: 52,000 sustainer. 4600	61.5
Propulsion System	Booster (rocket) & sustainer	———
Propellants	Booster: solid sustainer: JP	Solid
Weight (lbs)	12,000	10.5

 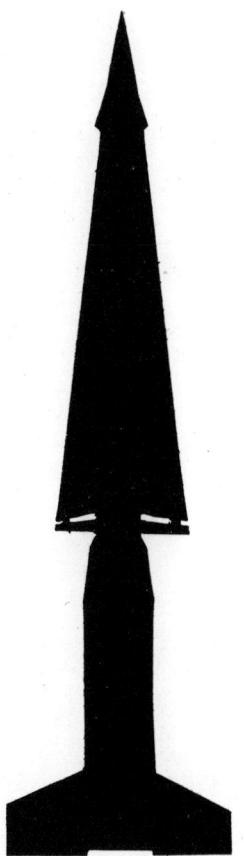 

Nike-Ajax	**Nike-Hercules**	**Polaris**
Army	Army	Navy
Surface-to-air	Surface-to-air	Surface-to-surface
Command	Command	Inertial
35 max.	75 max.	1500
1500 mph	2200 mph (approx.)	6000 mph (average)
2600	———	80,000-100,000
Booster (rocket) & sustainer	Booster (rocket) & sustainer	2-stage rocket
Booster: solid sustainer: nitric acid & JP	Solid	Solid
2000+ (plus booster)	———	28,000

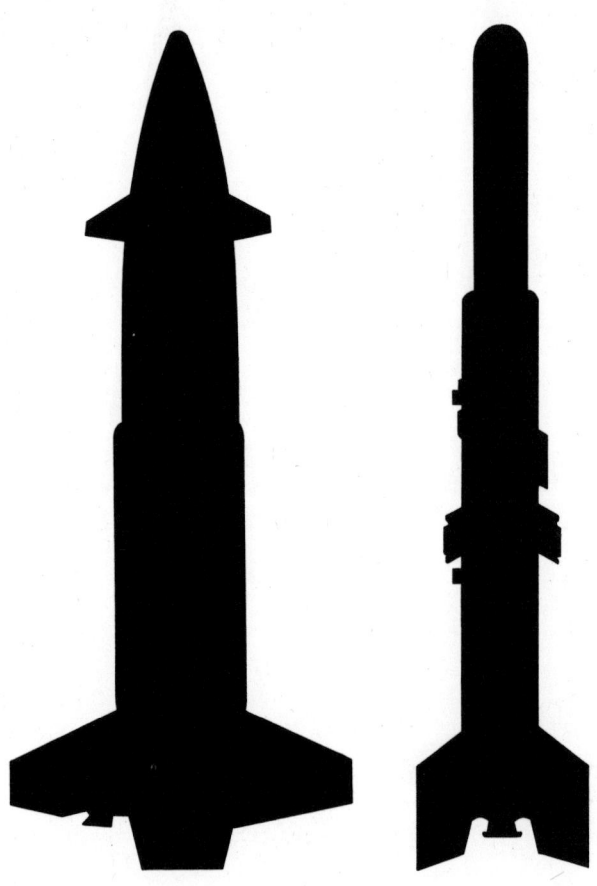

MISSILE DATA (cont.)

	Rascal	**Rat**
Service	Air Force	Navy
Type	Air-to-surface	Anti-submarine
Guidance	Radar command	Acoustical
Range (*miles*)	100 max.	5
Velocity	Mach 1.5 max.	————
Thrust (*lbs*)	12,000	————
Propulsion System	Rocket	Rocket-boosted homing torpedo
Propellants	Liquid oxygen & alcohol	(Booster) Solid
Weight (*lbs*)	13,000	450

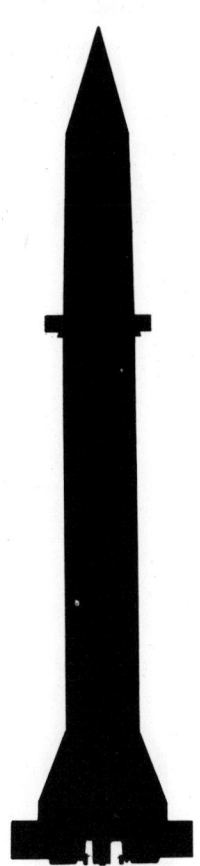  

Redstone	Regulus I	Regulus II
Army	Navy	Navy
Surface-to-surface	Surface-to-surface	Surface-to-surface
Inertial	Command	Command or inertial
180-250	500	1000
———	Mach 0.9	Mach 2
75,000	4600	15,000
Rocket	Booster (rocket) & sustainer	Booster (rocket) & sustainer
Liquid oxygen & alcohol	Booster: solid sustainer: JP	Booster: solid sustainer: JP
45,000	12,000 (less booster)	22,000 (less booster)

MISSILE DATA (cont.)

	Sergeant	**Sidewinder**
Service	Army	Navy
Type	Surface-to-surface	Air-to-air
Guidance	Inertial	Infrared homing
Range (miles)	100+	6-7
Velocity	———	Mach 2.5
Thrust (lbs)	50,000+	———
Propulsion System	Rocket	Rocket
Propellants	Solid	Solid
Weight (lbs)	20,000-25,000	55

Snark	**Sparrow III**	**T-1**
Air Force	Navy	USSR
Surface-to-surface	Air-to-air	Surface-to-surface
Stellar inertial	Radar homing	Radio-inertial
5000-6500	5-8	400-600
Mach 0.9 max.	Mach 2.5-3	4400 mph
66,000		77,000-78,000
Rocket-boosted jet	Rocket	Rocket
Booster: Solid	Solid	Oxygen/alcohol
Sustainer: Liquid		
50,000 (approx.)	350	38,000

MISSILE DATA (cont.)

	T-2	**T-3**
Service	USSR	USSR
Type	Surface-to-surface	Surface-to-surface
Guidance	Radio-inertial	Radio-inertial
Range (*miles*)	1800	5000
Velocity	5200 mph	15,000 mph
Thrust (*lbs*)	77,000-78,000	270,000
Propulsion System	Booster & sustainer rockets	Booster & sustainer rockets
Propellants	Oxygen/alcohol	Oxygen/kerosene
Weight (*lbs*)	122,000	165,000-175,000

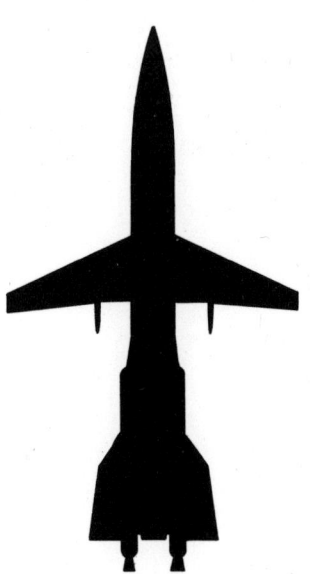

T-3A	**T-4**	**T-4A**
USSR	USSR	USSR
Surface-to-surface	Surface-to-surface	Surface-to-surface
Radio-inertial	Radio-inertial	Boost-glide
6200	1000	12,000
16,000 mph	9500 mph	14,000-15,000 mph
270,000	53,000	————
Booster & sustainer rockets	Booster & sustainer rockets	————
Liquid oxygen/kerosene	Oxygen/hydrazine	————
185,000	71,000	232,000

MISSILE DATA (cont.)

	T-5	**T-5B**
Service	USSR	USSR
Type	Surface-to-surface	Surface-to-surface
Guidance	None	None
Range (miles)	100	25
Velocity	2900 mph	————
Thrust (lbs)	(1) 83,500, (2) 2300, (3) 440	————
Propulsion System	3-stage rocket	Rocket
Propellants	(1) Nitric acid / hydrazine, (2) & (3) SPR's	————
Weight (lbs)	4850	————

T-5C	T-6	T-7
USSR	USSR	USSR
Surface-to-surface	Surface-to-air	Surface-to-air
	Radar	Inertial
———	———	———
15-20		
———	1630 mph	3350 mph
———	10,000	11,000
Rocket	Booster (rocket) & sustainer	———
Solid	Solid	Liquid oxygen & hydrazine
4400	4000	5050

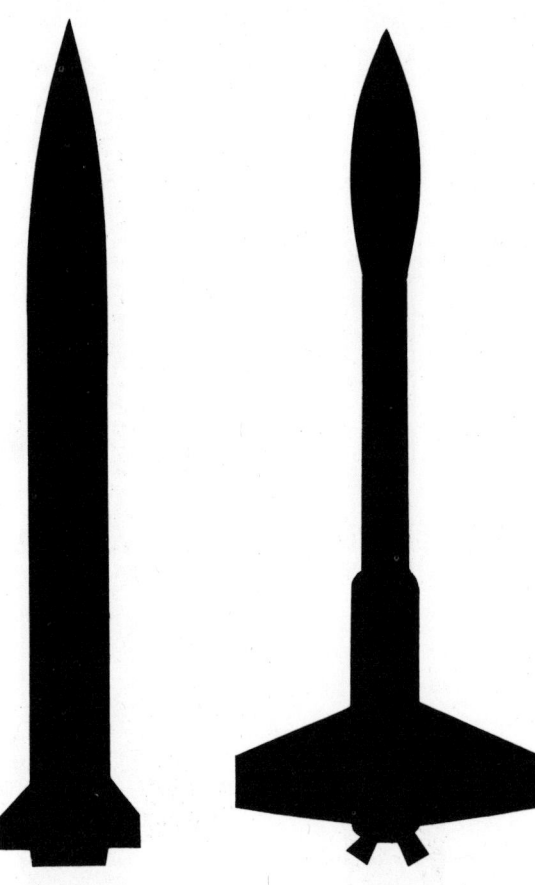

MISSILE DATA (cont.)

	T-7A	**T-8**
Service	USSR	USSR
Type	Surface-to-surface	Surface-to-air
Guidance	Radio-inertial	Infrared
Range (miles)	100	15
Velocity	3200 mph	1450 mph
Thrust (lbs)	11,500	4600
Propulsion System	——	Booster (rocket) & sustainer
Propellants	Liquid oxygen & hydrazine	Booster: solid sustainer: Nitric acid/alcohol
Weight (lbs)	4500	1875

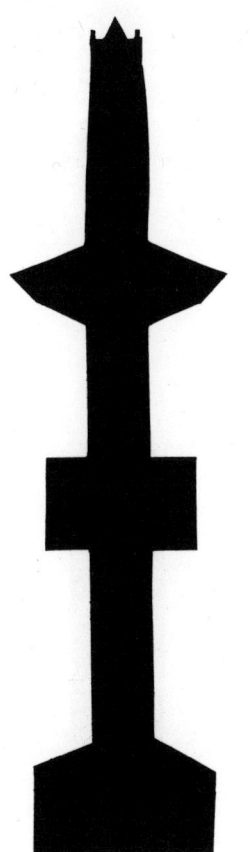 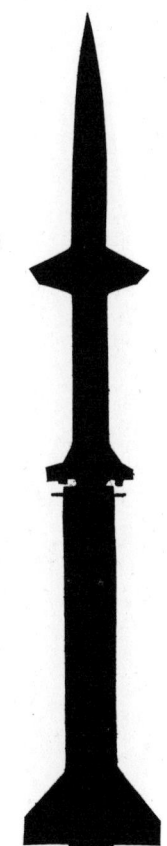 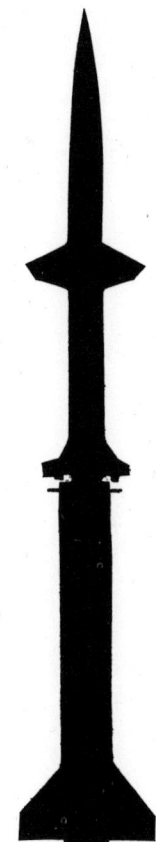

Talos	**Terrier I**	**Terrier II**
Navy	Navy	Navy
Surface-to-air	Surface-to-air	Surface-to-air
Beam rider/passive homing	Beam rider	Beam rider
70 (approx.)	10 max	20 max
Mach 3+	Mach 2.5	Max 2.5
———	———	———
Rocket-boosted ramjet	Booster & sustainer rockets	Booster & sustainer rockets
Booster: Solid Sustainer: JP	Solid	Solid
3000 (less booster)	1000	———

MISSILE DATA (cont.)

	Thor	**Titan**
Service	Air Force	Air Force
Type	IRBM	ICBM
Guidance	Inertial	Inertial/radio-inertial
Range (*miles*)	1500-2200	5500 max.
Velocity	10,000 mph max.	15,000 mph max.
Thrust (*lbs*)	165,000	300,000
Propulsion System	Rocket	2-stage rocket
Propellants	Liquid oxygen & kerosene	Liquid oxygen & JP-6
Weight (*lbs*)	100,000	222,000

Zuni

Navy
Air-to-air & air-to-sur-
  face
None
5 max.
Mach 3

———

Rocket
Solid
107

(All missile silhouettes are credited to (Missiles and
Rockets (American Aviation Publications) July 28,
1959)

DATA ON THE SOLAR SYSTEM PLANETS AND EARTH'S MOON

Name	Mean Distance from Sun (millions of miles)	Length of Year (earth time)	Length of Day (earth time)	Diameter (miles)	Gravity at Surface (in g's)	Escape Velocity (miles/ sec.)	Transit Time* from Earth	Surface Conditions
Sun	0	—	—	864,000	28.0	385.0	—	FH gas. Surface temperature: 11,000 degrees F.
Moon	238,857 (from earth)	27 hours 7 minutes 43 seconds (month)	27 hours 7 minutes 43 seconds	2,160	0.17	1.5	2.3 days	No atmosphere. Temperatures: At noon on the equator, over 212 degrees F; at midnight, —200 degrees F.
Mercury	36.0	87.97 days	87.97 days	3,010	0.4	2.6	110 days	Same face always turned to the sun. No atmosphere. Temperatures: Bright side, 770 degrees F (above melting point of lead and tin); dark side, close to absolute zero.
Venus	67.2	224.70 days	30 days?	7,580	0.9	6.4	150 days	Atmosphere contains much carbon dioxide, possibly some nitrogen, argon, and formaldehyde. No oxygen or water detected. Temperatures: Daytime, 140 degrees F; nighttime, —9°F. Huge dust storms.
Earth	92.9	365.26 days	23 hours 56 minutes	7,918	1.00	7.0	—	Atmosphere; nitrogen, oxygen, carbon dioxide, water vapor, rare gases. Temperatures: maximum recorded, 125 degrees F; minimum recorded, —90 degrees F. Surface 0.71 ocean.
Mars	141.5	686.98 days	24 hours 37 minutes	4,220	0.4	3.2	260 days	Atmosphere very thin, probably contains water vapor but little or no oxygen or carbon dioxide. Temperatures low; highest recorded, 86 degrees F in summer at equator. Ice, snow at poles. Possibly some lichens; animal life improbable. No mountains.
Jupiter	483.3	11.86 years	9 hours 50 minutes (approx.)	87,000	2.7	37.3	2.7 years	Extensive atmosphere, largely methane and ammonia; at bottom, pressure over a million earth atmospheres. Maximum temperature: —216 degrees F.
Saturn	886	29.46 years	10 hours 15 minutes (approx.)	72,000	1.2	23.9	6 years	Similar to Jupiter. Maximum temperature: —243 degrees F.
Uranus	1,783	84.0 years	10 hours 8 minutes (approx.)	31,000	1.0	13.0	16 years	Atmosphere: methane with only a trace of ammonia. Maximum temperature: —300 degrees F.
Neptune	2,793	164.8 years	16 hours?	33,000	1.0	14.0	31 years	Similar to Uranus. Maximum temperature: —330 degrees F.
Pluto	3,666**	247.7 years	?	8,000?	?	?	46 years	Unknown.

* For coasting flight at minimum launch velocity.
** Orbit has considerable eccentricity.

128